THE NEW ILLUSTRATED

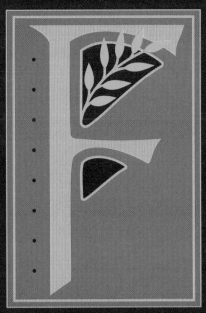

FAMILY HYMN

BOOK

Featuring designs from the Hallmark Collection

Arranged by PHILLIP KEVEREN

With an Introduction and background text for the hymns by Dr. William J. Reynolds, Professor of Church Music at Southwestern Baptist Theological Seminary

ISBN 0-7935-1653-6

Hal Leonard Publishing Corporation

7777 West Bluemound Road P.O. Box 13819 Milwaukee, WI 53213

Published by HAL LEONARD PUBLISHING CORPORATION
P.O. Box 13819, 7777 West Bluemound Road
Milwaukee, WI 53213 USA

Printed in Hong Kong

CONTENTS

Introit to the Mass for Church Dedication from a Czech gradual (book of chants for the mass), 1557. The two texts, one of which starts at the top of the page and the second of which starts on the penultimate line, are both in Czech. Vienna, Österreichische Nationalbibliothek.

PREFACE

Over the centuries, many composers have been inspired by their religious faith to write some of the world's most beautiful and treasured music. Hymns are very much a part of this vast musical heritage.

We have selected 50 of the world's most popular hymns, decorated them with designs from Hallmark, and included a brief history of each one. We hope that your family enjoys gathering together to sing and play this wonderful music, and *The New Illustrated Family Hymn Book* will be a center for enjoyment and closeness in your home for many years to come.

INTRODUCTION

French, School of Picardie, Thuison-les-Abbeville Altarpiece: The Last Supper, oil on panel, c. 1480, 117.2 x 50.9 cm, Mr. and Mrs. Martin A. Ryerson Collection, 1933. 1056

Hymn singing, as practiced in churches today, is deeply rooted in the Judeo-Christian tradition. Old Testament writings give evidence of psalm singing by the Children of Israel. The 150 psalms in the Hebrew Psalter are songs of great diversity that mirror the basic theological beliefs of the Jews. "Blessed is the man" is the opening phrase of Psalm 1 and "Praise ye the Lord" is the final phrase of Psalm 150. These eight words bracket the beginning and ending of the movement from finite mankind to an infinite God.

The largest category of psalms – 74 of the 150 – comprises expressions of praise, either directly or indirectly, to God. Fifty-six psalms are prayers of lamentation to God that are sung in the midst of stress and difficulty. Eleven psalms, called "Royal Psalms," celebrate David's rule in Jerusalem and that of his dynasty. Nine psalms, called "Wisdom Psalms," are wise sayings exhorting the people to live the good life and avoid ungodly living. These four classifications provide a wide variety of songs for singing

When the Christian era dawned, those who followed Jesus Christ continued to sing psalms. This is evident in the accounts of the Passover Supper in the gospels of Matthew and Mark; Jesus and his disciples, when they had concluded the supper, sang a hymn. Scholars believe that hymn to have been a portion of four psalms – 115, 116, 117, 118. Singing a hymn at the Last Supper was not something new that Jesus initiated. It was a regular part of the Passover celebration that commemorated the Israelites' release from bondage in Egypt. Further evidence of hymn singing from the pages of the New Testament is found in the account of Paul and Silas, who, imprisoned at Philippi, prayed and sang praises at midnight. An earthquake occurred, jail doors were opened, and the prisoners were freed (Acts 16:26).

The Hebrew Psalter and the manner in which it was used provided the musical heritage of the early Christians. New Testament accounts tell of the attendance of Jesus and his disciples at Temple worship, in which psalms were sung. The early Christians continued to sing the Old Testament psalms and added new songs – hymns – they had written that sang of Jesus Christ. Within decades after Pentecost, Christians were singing hymns; witness the apostle Paul's exhortation for believers to address one another "in psalms and hymns and spiritual songs" (Ephesians 5:19).

The hymn-like structure of some of the writings of Paul suggests that these were songs that were known to the churches to whom he wrote. For example:

Eye hath not seen,
    nor ear heard,
neither have entered into the heart of man,
    the things which God hath prepared
    for them that love him.
            1 Corinthians 2:9

Awake thou that sleepest,
    and rise from the dead,
    and Christ shall give thee light.
            Ephesians 5:14

Now unto the King eternal,
    immortal, invisible,
    the only wise God,
    be honor and glory
    forever and ever.
            1 Timothy 1:17

God was manifest in the flesh,
    justified in the Spirit,
    seen of angels,
    preached unto the Gentiles,
    believed on in the world,
    received up into glory.
            1 Timothy 3:16

Even the English translations reveal the lyrical quality of these lines.

Following the destruction of the Temple in Jerusalem in A.D. 70, the persecution of believers increased. Meetings of Christians for praise and fellowship were held in secret. Only those elements of Christian worship that believers deemed appropriate to their needs were kept. In the early centuries, a distinction emerged between clergy and laity that developed into a system of patriarchs, priests, bishops, and deacons. The clergy assumed a greater responsibility for Christian worship, forming and shaping the liturgy and the music that was involved.

At the time of Christ, Greek culture was the dominant influence throughout the Roman Empire. Greek was the language of the church, and remained so for 300 years, even in Rome. One of the earliest Greek hymns, dating from the third century and of unknown authorship, is "Phōs hilaron" (cheerful light). Known as the "Lamplighting Hymn," it was sung in the evening service at the lighting of lamps, probably in caves, caverns, or catacombs. The Greek hymn still forms part of the evening service of the Orthodox Church. Here is the first stanza of John Keble's English translation of 1834:

Hail, gladdening Light,
    of his pure glory poured
    Who is the immortal Father, heavenly blest,
    Holiest of Holies, Jesus Christ our Lord.

Clement of Alexandria (c. 170 – c. 220), Synesius of Cyrene (c. 375 – c. 414), Andrew of Crete (660 – 732), and John of Damascus (d.c. 780) all wrote Greek hymns.

Gradually the influence of Greek culture declined; and beginning in the fourth century, Latin began to replace Greek as the language of the Western church. This had become almost universal by the end of the sixth century. Hymns were written in Latin by many writers, among the most prolific of which were Hilary, Bishop of Poitiers (c. 310 – 366); Ambrose, Bishop of Milan (340 – 397); Venantius Fortunatus (c. 530 – 609); Theodulph of Orleans (c. 760 – 821); and Rabanus Maurus (d. 856).

At the beginning of the seventh century, the tunes that were used for the singing of these Latin hymns were gathered together. This work is generally attributed to Pope Gregory I (540 – 604), which accounts for their being referred to as Gregorian chants.

Three pages from a Sarum prayer book circa A.D. 1400. The Sarum Rite is a British modification of the Roman Catholic mass.

Annunciation to the Virgin, 1450/1460, Tempera and gold leaf on vellum, leaf from a Choir Book (Antiphonary) (NGA Miniatures 20), .589 x .425 (23¹/₈ x 16¹/₄), National Gallery of Art, Washington, Rosenwald Collection.

THE SIXTEENTH CENTURY

When Christopher Columbus discovered the New World in 1492, a nine-year-old lad was growing up in Germany who was destined to change Christian history. Martin Luther, the central figure of the Protestant Reformation in Germany, translated both Old and New Testaments into the German language and also wrote 37 hymns. For the first time Germans could read God's Word and sing his praise in their mother tongue. Luther believed that music was a gift from God and should be used in accomplishing the work of God. Luther's most famous hymn, "A Mighty Fortress Is Our God," based on Psalm 46, was written in 1529 during his struggle against the Roman Catholic Church.

Another important figure in the Protestant Reformation was John Calvin, a Frenchman who became pastor of a church in Geneva, Switzerland, in 1541. The focus of Calvin's theology was the truth of the Bible and the sovereignty of God. Because he opposed the rituals and ceremonies of the Roman Church, his worship services were dignified yet simple and consisted of preaching, praying, and singing. Only the psalms – in the vernacular of the people – were sung, and these were sung in unison without instrumental accompaniment.

Calvin entrusted the translation of the Hebrew psalms into French poetry to Clement Marot (c. 1497 – 1544) and later to Theodore Beza (1519 – 1605). Louis Bourgeois (c. 1510 – c. 1561) became Calvin's music editor, composing, arranging, and notating melodies for these French metrical psalms. The completed *Genevan Psalter* appeared in 1562.

About the same time that psalm singing began in Calvin's church in Geneva, Thomas Sternhold, Groom of the Royal Wardrobe of Henry VIII, began experimenting with the making of metrical psalms in English and, with the help of John Hopkins, produced an English psalter in 1562, *The Whole Booke of Psalms Translated into English Metre.*

Martin Luther

The persecution of Protestants by Queen Mary, 1553 – 1558, caused many people to leave England and settle temporarily on the Continent. Some went to Geneva, visited Calvin's church, and were greatly impressed by the sound of the psalm singing. An English church was established in Geneva in 1555 with John Knox as pastor; the following year a partial psalter was prepared for this congregation. By 1560, after the death of Queen Mary, many of the refugees had returned home to England and Scotland, bringing with them the influence of Genevan psalm singing. Because of this, many collections of psalms and psalm tunes were published and a standard practice of psalm singing was established in England and Scotland.

French immigrants to the coast of South Carolina and Florida in 1562 – 1565 brought the first French metrical psalms and psalm tunes to the American soil. Native Indians learned them and sang them long after the French settlements had been wiped out by the Spaniards.

Sir Francis Drake and his men brought the first English psalms and psalm tunes to the coast of northern California in June of 1579. These men camped ashore for five weeks, making repairs to their ships. Psalms were sung in the daily religious services, and the friendly Indians who visited the camp learned to sing them. Francis Fletcher, Drake's chaplain, reported that the Indians "took such pleasure in our singing of Psalmes." The singing of French psalms on the east coast and of English psalms on the west coast was a meager beginning for Christian song in what would become, 200 years later, the United States of America.

John Calvin

HE SEVENTEENTH CENTURY

On the Continent, the Thirty Years' War, 1618 – 48, had a significant influence on German hymnody. Beginning as a Roman Catholic-Protestant conflict, the long war resulted in a political and religious battle involving, at one time or another, the entire European continent. The German provinces of Silesia and Saxony became the battlefields where several nations fought for three decades.

During the conflict Martin Rinkart was the Lutheran pastor in the walled city of Eilenburg in Saxony. He ministered midst the famine, pestilence, and destruction to the throngs of people who sought refuge in the city and became casualties of the war. During the pestilence of 1637, he conducted 4,500 burial services – sometimes 40 or 50 a day. Frail in body but heroic in character, Rinkart in 1636 wrote "Now Thank We All Our God," one of the great Lutheran hymns from this era.

In 1630, a group of Puritans from England came to the New World and became known as the Massachusetts Bay Colony. They brought the psalters they had used in England, but soon began to feel that the translations were too liberal for their use. John Cotton and other clergymen set about to make a new metrical translation of the Hebrew psalms. It was published in 1640 – *The Whole Booke of Psalmes Faithfully Translated into English Metre.* Known as the "Bay Psalm Book," it was the first book of any kind to be published in the American colonies. The version of Psalm 23 reveals the style of these translations:

> The Lord to mee a shepheard is,
>   want therefore shall not I.
> Hee in the folds of tender-grasse,
>   doth cause mee downe to lie:
> To waters calme me gently leads
>   Restore my soule doth hee:
> he doth in paths of righteousness:
>   for his names sake leade mee.
> Yea though in valley of deaths shade
>   I walk, none ill I'le feare:

> because thou art with mee, thy rod,
>   and staffe my comfort are.
> For mee a table thou hast spread,
>   in presence of my foes:
> thou dost annoynt my head with oyle,
>   my cup it over-flowes.
> Goodnes & mercy surely shall
>   all my dayes follow mee:
> and in the Lords house I shall dwell
>   so long as dayes shall bee.

And the psalm singing took root in the American colonies.

In England, psalm singing continued in the seventeenth century, and metrical versions of psalms and new psalm tunes were published. Thomas Ken, of the faculty of Winchester College, published *A Manual of Prayers for the Use of the Scholars of Winchester College* in 1674. He included three hymns to be sung in the morning, in the evening, and at midnight. Each hymn had the same concluding stanza:

> Praise God from whom all blessings flow,
> Praise him all creatures here below;
> Praise him above ye heavenly host,
> Praise Father, Son, and Holy Ghost.

Those who did not conform to the beliefs and practices of the Church of England were called Nonconformists or Dissenters. Today in England and Wales, these terms are applied to Baptists, Congregationalists, Presbyterians, Methodists, and Unitarians, and to other independent groups. (In Scotland, because the established church is Presbyterian, other churches, including the Church of England, are considered Nonconformists.) It was the Nonconformists who were responsible for the rise of hymn singing in England.

In the late seventeenth century, a major conflict arose in Baptist churches in England over hymn singing. Congregations were split and families divided over this practice. The leading advocate for singing hymns was Benjamin Keach, pastor of the Baptist church in Southwark, out from London. Because Scripture records that Christ and his disciples sang a hymn at the conclusion of the Last Supper, Keach felt justified in leading his church to follow this example. In 1691, he published a collection of 300 hymns and led Baptists, in spite of opposition, to accept hymn singing.

THE EIGHTEENTH CENTURY

Isaac Watts

By 1700, the harassment and buffeting of Nonconformists was over, and there was ushered in what has been called the "Century of Divine Songs." Isaac Watts (1674 – 1748), the product of a Nonconformist home, published his first book of hymns in 1707, entitled *Hymns and Spiritual Songs.* Twelve years later he published *The Psalms of David imitated in the Language of the New Testament.* Watts believed that the New Testament church should sing the psalms of David in the spirit of the New Testament. In other words, he wanted David to speak like a Christian. His version of Psalm 90 begins "Jesus shall reign where'er the sun." In the decades that followed, *Dr. Watts's Psalms and Hymns* were bound together, published in many editions, and widely used both in England and in the American colonies. For Nonconformist churches these provided the main body of congregational song for almost two centuries.

An amusing incident occurred in the colonies during the Revolutionary War. A group of soldiers of the Continental Army was attacked by British troops near a small church building. For their guns, the colonists needed gunpowder, shot, and wadding, but discovered their supply of wadding was gone. One ingenious soldier ran into the church and returned with several copies of *Dr. Watts's Psalms and Hymns.* He began tearing pages from the books and making wadding out of them, yelling to his comrades as he did so, "Give 'em Watts! boys, Give 'em Watts!"

A dozen or more of Watts's hymns and psalms may be found in our most recent hymnals, more than 250 years after they were written. Some of his hymns in great favor with American congregations today are "Alas, and did my Savior bleed," "Am I a soldier of the cross," "Come, we that love the Lord," "Give me the wings of faith," "I sing th'almighty power of God," "Jesus shall reign where'er the sun," "Joy to the world! the Lord is come," "O God, our help in ages past," "This is the day the Lord hath made," and "When I survey the wondrous cross," which has been called "the greatest hymn in the English language":

> When I survey the wondrous cross
>   On which the Prince of Glory died,
> My richest gain I count but loss,
>   And pour contempt on all my pride.
>
> Forbid it, Lord, that I should boast,
>   Save in the death of Christ, my God;
> All the vain things that charm me most,
>   I sacrifice them to his blood.
>
> See from his head, his hands, his feet
>   Sorrow and love flow mingled down;
> Did e'er such love and sorrow meet,
>   Or thorns compose so rich a crown?
>
> His dying crimson, like a robe,
>   Spreads o'er his body on the tree;
> Then I am dead to all the globe,
>   And all the globe is dead to me.
>
> Were the whole realm of nature mine,
>   That were a present far too small;
> Love so amazing, so divine
>   Demands my soul, my life, my all.

With his New Testament open to Galatians 6:14, Isaac Watts "surveys" the crucifixion of our Lord in vivid language. He pictures the cross, not as a "cruel" cross, nor the "old rugged" cross, but as the "wondrous" cross. Wondrous, because Christ's death on the cross provided salvation for mankind.

Others had written hymns earlier, and Benjamin Keach is credited with beginning the practice of congregational hymn singing that permeated Nonconformist churches and eventually the Church of England. But it was Isaac Watts who opened the door to a new era and a new day in Christian song.

A monument honoring his memory stands in Bunhill Fields, the Dissenters' burying ground on City Road in London. The inscription reads:

> Ages unborn will make his songs
> The joy and labor of their tongues.

Hymn singing in England, and eventually the rest of the world, has been enriched by the poetic skill of Charles Wesley (1707–1778). Charles and his brother, John (1703–1791), grew up at Epworth, England, in the home of the parish minister. Both were students at Christ Church College, Oxford, both were ordained in the Church of England, and both had a spiritual experience that changed their lives.

Because of their fervent preaching, Anglican leaders forbade them to preach in the churches. To the fields, the mines, the prisons, and in barns and buildings the two brothers went to proclaim the gospel. Charles' phenomenal hymn writing produced more than 6,000 hymns that John published in 56 collections of hymns over a period of 53 years. Among the most frequently sung today of Charles Wesley's hymns are "Christ the Lord is risen today," "Hark, the herald angels sing," "Jesus, lover of my soul," "Love divine, all loves excelling," "O for a thousand tongues to sing," "Rejoice the Lord is King," "And can it be that I should gain," and "Ye servants of God, your Master proclaim."

In these hymns was a new evangelical emphasis. Christ's unlimited atonement, which they preached, was also sung from the pages of their hymnals. In addition to these hymns of the free gospel, they provided hymns of Christian experience for public worship or private devotion. Today hymnals around the world, in English and many other languages, include the Wesley hymns. *The United Methodist Hymnal* (1989) includes 51 hymns by Charles Wesley. What a magnificent treasure!

In 1779 John Newton, Anglican minister in the English village of Olney, published *Olney Hymns*, to which he contributed 280 hymns. Among these were "Amazing grace! how sweet the sound," "Glorious things of thee are spoken," and "How sweet the name of Jesus sounds." Newton's friend William Cowper contributed 68 hymns to this collection, including "God moves in a mysterious way" and "There is a fountain filled with blood."

THE NINETEENTH CENTURY

It was not until after the American colonies became the United States with its remarkable constitution that the psalms and hymns of Isaac Watts were widely sung in America. Numerous editions of Watts's works, with hymns from other sources, were published on this side of the Atlantic, and American congregations sang predominantly these hymns for the first half of the century. In 1801, Timothy Dwight, president of Yale, published one such collection and included his own version of Psalm 137, "I love thy kingdom, Lord." This is probably the earliest American hymn that remains in common usage.

The Church of England sang only the psalms until 1820, when the singing of hymns was permitted, and the quantity of new hymns greatly increased. Hymns of didactic design and utilitarian purpose gave way to hymns of poetic feeling and literary merit. Hymn writers began to write hymns accommodating the *Book of Common Prayer*, the rituals and services of the Church, and the liturgical year.

The Oxford Movement, designed to bring about a spiritual renewal in the Church, dates from the third decade of the nineteenth century. It was an attempt to recover the ideals of the pre-Reformation church. The movement brought many changes to the Church, and had an impact on the hymns of the period. Reginald Heber's "Holy, holy, holy," John Keble's "Sun of my soul, thou Savior dear," and John Henry Newman's "Lead, kindly light" are examples of the new hymns. Some writers, with linguistic skills in Latin, German, and Greek, discovered early Christian hymns and, retaining the spirit of the devoted believers who had sung them, translated them into nineteenth-century language. Examples of some excellent translations are Edward Caswall's "When morning gilds the skies," John Mason Neale's "All glory, laud, and honor," and Catherine Winkworth's "Now thank we all our God."

The hymnody of the Oxford Movement culminated in the publication in 1861 in London of *Hymns Ancient and Modern*, a significant hymnal. Here were appropriate hymns for days of the week, feasts, fasts, services of the *Book of Common Prayer*, saints' days, and other occasions. It was a benchmark in English hymnody and of significant influence in both England and America.

A distinctive characteristic of the Victorian hymns reflected the need for a hymn to have its own tune, replacing the older practice of using common tunes – Common Meter, Long Meter, Short Meter, etc. – for any text of the same meter. Composers such as John B. Dykes, William H. Monk, George Elvey, Henry Smart, Arthur Sullivan, and Samuel Sebastian Wesley were foremost in composing Victorian hymn tunes. Their names are still found in our hymnals.

Hymns of social concern, hymns expressing an awareness of human rights and human needs, surfaced first in the United States. The gathering stormclouds of anti-slavery feelings that resulted in the Civil War may be seen in some hymns of that era. The original texts of Edmund Sears' "It came upon the midnight clear" (1849) and Henry W. Longfellow's "I heard the bells on Christmas day" (1864) contained strong words against slavery. The boldest lines have been edited out of our hymnals long ago. James Russell Lowell's "Once to every man and nation" (1845) was written as a protest against the Mexican War and the admission of slave states to the union. Washington Gladden, a Congregational minister, was an early exponent of the social implications of the gospel. He aided in the exposure of the "Tweed Ring," politicians who controlled New York City's treasury and made off with millions of dollars. He spoke out boldly against the unfair and monopolistic practices of big business. In 1879 he wrote "O Master, let me walk with thee." Here is his second stanza, usually omitted from our hymnals:

Arthur Sullivan

> O Master, let me walk with thee
> Before the taunting Pharisee;
> Help me to bear the sting of spite,
> The hate of men who hide thy light,
> The sore distrust of souls sincere
> Who cannot read thy judgments clear,
> The dullness of the multitude,
> Who dimly guess that thou art good.

In 1866, Fisk University at Nashville, Tennessee, began as one of the schools established in the South to educate slaves freed by the Emancipation Proclamation. A group from Fisk, called the Jubilee Singers, began in 1871 to sing spirituals beyond the campus in Nashville. In a few months, their concerts raised $150,000 for the school and public response was overwhelming. After much success in the major cities of the North and East, they introduced spirituals to England, Scotland, and Ireland, and to Germany. Despite the popularity of such spirituals as "Were you there," "Standing in the need of prayer," "Swing low, sweet chariot," "Go, tell it on the mountain," "There is a balm in Gilead," and many others, they were not accepted into the body of American hymnals until the last half of the twentieth century. These Afro-American spirituals have greatly enriched our Christian song.

In 1872, evangelists Dwight L. Moody and Ira D. Sankey visited England, and the gospel songs sung and taught by Sankey found fertile soil in the crowds that thronged to their meetings. So popular were these songs that a London publisher brought out a 24-page pamphlet of Sankey's songs in 1873. Subsequent enlarged editions were published, and by 1903 contained 1,200 songs.

When Moody and Sankey returned to America in 1875, the rapid growth of the Sunday School movement and the Young Men's Christian Association, and the Second Great Awakening of the 1850s, had resulted in a ready acceptance of the gospel song. This musical genre had roots in American folk hymnody, camp meeting songs, singing school songs, and Sunday school songs. Some of the most popular gospel songs today first appeared in the small collections designed for the Sunday school. Among these are "To God be the glory," "I am thine, O Lord," and "Jesus loves me, this I know." They were never intended to be sung in church services. More than any other lyric writer, Fanny J. Crosby, the blind poet, captured the spirit of the time in her gospel song texts. Other prolific composers of such tunes were William B. Bradbury, Philip P. Bliss, James McGranahan, George C. Stebbins, and Charles H. Gabriel. In the evangelical churches of the Free Church tradition, the gospel song found wide acceptance and became a standard staple well into the twentieth century.

THE TWENTIETH CENTURY

The break away from Victorian hymnody, after its half century of dominance, emerged in *The English Hymnal* (London, 1906). Percy Dearmer, Anglican clergyman, served as editor, and enlisted the talents of young Ralph Vaughan Williams as music editor. These two also were responsible for *Songs of Praise* (1925, revised and enlarged 1931), an adventuresome hymnal.

For example, Dearmer remembered a Gaelic folk tune from his childhood and thought it worthy of congregational song. He asked Eleanor Farjeon to write a text for this tune of unusual meter (5.5.5.4.D.) and suggested thanksgiving for a new day as its subject. "Morning has broken" was the result of her efforts.

In 1972 Cat Stevens, the British popular singer, recorded an album in which he included "Morning has broken." The album reached the top of the pop charts, and "Morning has broken" became very well known. What Americans thought was a British "pop" tune turned out to be a hymn from a Church of England hymnal.

The gospel songs inundated many parts of the world during the twentieth century. These songs, which originated in America, were carried in Spanish and Portuguese versions to South America and to many other countries of the world. The success achieved by this musical culture defies description. As George Beverly Shea sang "How Great Thou Art" throughout the world in the Billy Graham Crusades, through radio, television, and recordings, the song became a strong symbol of this genre.

Capital District Billy Graham Crusade, Knickerbocker Arena, Albany, New York – July, 1990.

Harry Emerson Fosdick, while awaiting the completion of Riverside Church in New York City, wrote "God of Grace and God of Glory" in the summer of 1930. Here is one of the finest hymns written in the first half of the century. Fosdick's hymn was written to be sung to the tune REGENT SQUARE, but Robert G. McCutchan set it to the Welsh tune CWM RHONDDA in the 1935 *Methodist Hymnal,* and this wedding of text and tune became a lasting union. Fosdick was furious when he learned of the change and said, "They have ruined my hymn, and the Methodists did it!" But Fosdick's judgment was wrong.

Of the publishing of new hymnals in the twentieth century there seems to be no end. Each decade has brought forth new collections combining old and new hymns designed for the perceived needs of various congregations of Christian folk. New sounds in church music emerged in England in the mid fifties, and such terms as "light," "pop," and "folk" were new labels for church music. An emphasis on youth brought new sounds, new songs, and new experiences, a decade later in the United States. Guitars, trumpets, drum sets, etc., were heard in churches where such sounds had not been heard before. Some congregations welcomed the new music joyfully, while others listened with much apprehension. After a couple of decades, the use of guitars and drums diminished, but church music has not been the same again. There has remained a bit more openness to new songs and new sounds and this has been healthful.

A spate of the writing of new hymns appeared first in England. An early pioneer was George W. Briggs (1875–1956), an evangelical Anglican minister. Beginning in the 1920s, his hymns, expressing new ideas in simple vocabulary, pointed the way for others.

Following World War II, a new ecumenical spirit appeared. Here was a willingness to change traditional practices and a concern for greater participation in the hymn singing. In the early 1960s new hymns by heretofore unknown writers and composers make their appearance: Erik Routley (1917–1982), Timothy Dudley-Smith (b. 1926),

Brian Wren (b. 1936), Fred Pratt Green (b. 1901), and Fred Kaan (b. 1926). These five individuals were an interesting mix of personalities. Dudley-Smith was Anglican, Green was Methodist, and Routley, Wren, and Kaan were of the Congregational branch of what became, in 1972, the United Reformed Church of England.

Green owes much of his success to Routley, who not only encouraged his hymn writing, but also promoted the singing of his hymns in both England and America. Though Routley was not as prolific in hymn writing or hymn tune composing as others, he was a central figure in the sixties and seventies, especially in his many writings on hymnody and church music. He believed Green to be the most significant hymn writer of Methodism since Charles Wesley 200 years earlier.

Probably the best known of Green's hymns is one written in 1972 at the request of John Wilson, music teacher at Charterhouse, and the Royal College of Music. Wilson requested a hymn appropriate for a festival of praise or a choir anniversary, and suggested that it fit Charles V. Stanford's tune ENGELBERG. The result was "When in our music God is glorified." The wide acceptance of this hymn bespeaks Green's excellent writing.

Christian song is alive and well as we come to the end of the twentieth century. We glance back over 2,000 years since our Lord walked on this earth and thank God for all those who have written words and music, who have sung praise to God and proclaimed the gospel of Jesus Christ in song. To the heritage we have we add new songs of our day and sing joyfully.

Selah!

William J. Reynolds
Professor of Church Music
Southwestern Baptist Theological Seminary

CHRONOLOGICAL LISTING OF HYMNS

820   All glory, laud, and honor—Theodulph of Orleans
1529   A mighty fortress is our God—Martin Luther
1636   Now thank we all our God—Martin Rinkart
1677   Fairest Lord Jesus—Anon., German
1707   When I survey the wondrous cross—Isaac Watts
1739   Christ the Lord is risen today—Charles Wesley
1739   O for a thousand tongues to sing—Charles Wesley
1743   Love divine, all loves excelling—Charles Wesley
1757   Come, thou almighty King—Anon.
1775   Rock of ages—Augustus M. Toplady
1779   All hail the power of Jesus' name—Edward Perronet
1779   Amazing grace—John Newton
1787   How firm a foundation—Anon.
1826   Holy, holy, holy—Reginald Heber
1830   My faith looks up to thee—Ray Palmer
1834   Just as I am—Charlotte Elliott
1836   Savior, like a shepherd lead us—Anon.
1840   Nearer, my God, to thee—Sarah F. Adams
1840   Sweet hour of prayer—William Walford
1844   Come, ye thankful people, come—Henry Alford
1847   Abide with me—Henry F. Lyte
1849   Faith of our fathers—Frederick W. Faber
1855   What a friend we have in Jesus—Joseph Scriven
1858   Stand up, stand up for Jesus—George Duffield, Jr.
1860   Eternal Father, strong to save—William Whiting
1862   He leadeth me—Joseph H. Gilmore
1864   Onward, Christian soldiers—Sabine Baring-Gould
1866   I love to tell the story—Katherine Hankey
1866   The Church's one foundation—Samuel J. Stone
1868   In the sweet by and by—Sanford F. Bennett
1872   I need thee every hour—Annie S. Hawks
1873   Blessed assurance—Fanny J. Crosby
1874   Take my life and let it be—Frances R. Havergal
1875   I am thine, O Lord—Fanny J. Crosby
1876   God of our fathers—Daniel C. Roberts
1880   God be with you till we meet again—Jeremiah E. Rankin
1880   Softly and tenderly, Jesus is calling—Will L. Thompson
1883   Jesus is tenderly calling you home—Fanny J. Crosby
1886   How great thou art—Carl Boberg
1893   When the roll is called up yonder—James M. Black
1894   We gather together—Anon.
1901   This is my Father's world—Maltbie D. Babcock
1905   Be thou my vision—Ancient Irish, tr. Mary Byrne
1907   Have thine own way, Lord—Adelaide A. Pollard
1912   In the garden—C. Austin Miles
1913   The old rugged cross—George Bennard
1932   Precious Lord, take my hand—Thomas A. Dorsey
1939   Peace in the valley—Thomas A. Dorsey
1972   When in our music God is glorified—Fred Pratt Green
UNDATED—Let us break bread together

"AND I SAW THE NEW JERUSALEM COMING DOWN FROM GOD OUT OF HEAVEN". REV. XXI. 2

From the Hallmark Historical Collection. From an original 19th century greeting card published by Louis Prang of Boston.

A MIGHTY FORTRESS IS OUR GOD

Martin Luther's hymn has been called "the greatest hymn of the greatest man of the greatest period of German history." Based on Psalm 46, it was written in 1529, both words and music, during his intense struggle with the Roman Catholic Church. The hymn expressed his confidence of victory in that crisis. We can imagine him singing heartily the final lines:

> Let goods and kindred go,
> This mortal life also
> The body they may kill:
> God's truth abideth still
> His kingdom is forever.

A MIGHTY FORTRESS IS OUR GOD

Martin Luther, 1529

With grandeur

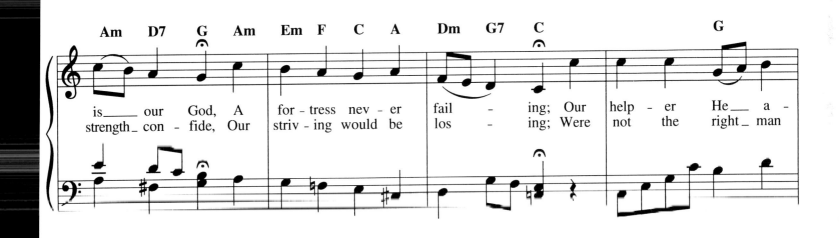

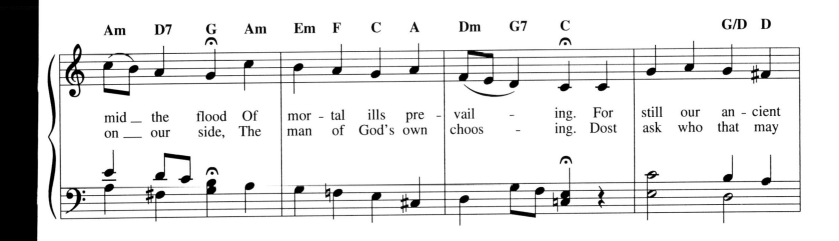

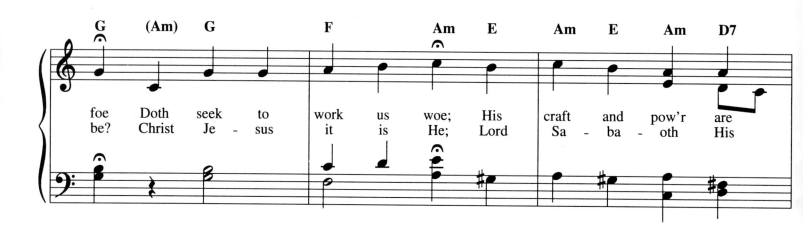

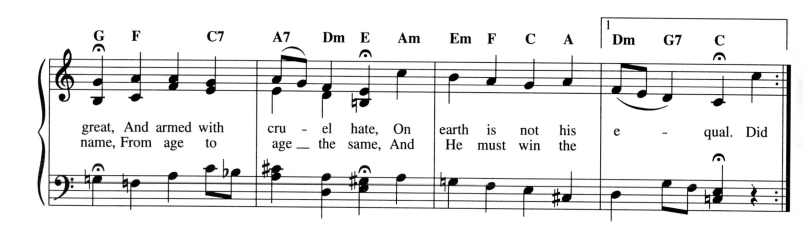

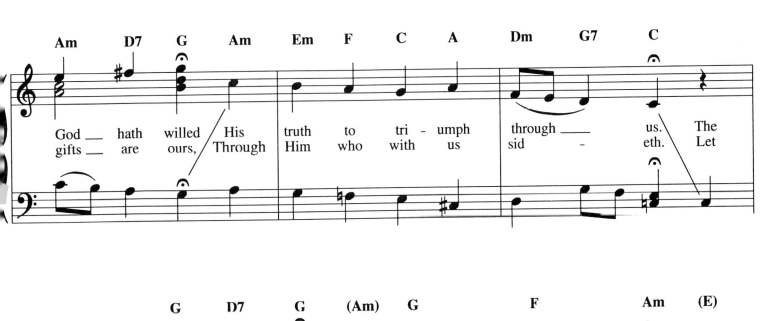

God __ hath willed / His truth to tri - umph through __ us. The
gifts __ are ours, / Through Him who with us sid - eth. Let

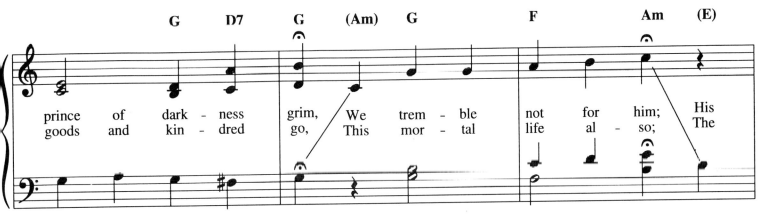

prince of dark - ness grim, / We trem - ble not for him; His
goods and kin - dred go, / This mor - tal life al - so; The

rage we can en - dure, / For lo! his doom __ is sure; One
bod - y they may kill; / God's truth a - bid - eth still; His

lit - tle word shall fell __ him. That
king - dom is for - ev - er.
rit.

"THE THORN BELOW - THE CROWN ABOVE"

From the Hallmark Historical Collection. *From an original 19th century greeting card published by De La Rue.*

ABIDE WITH ME

Henry Francis Lyte, a Church of England minister, wrote the hymn in 1847, as he concluded his 24-year ministry at Lower Brixham in Devonshire, England. The hymn tune was composed by William H. Monk for the hymn in 1861. Edith Cavell, an English nurse, heroine of World War I, sang the hymn as an expression of her faith as she faced a firing squad for assisting Allied soldiers to escape from German-occupied Belgium in 1915.

ABIDE WITH ME

Henry F. Lyte, 1847

EVENTIDE
W.H. Monk, 1861

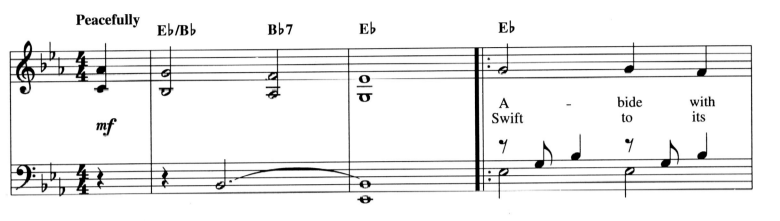

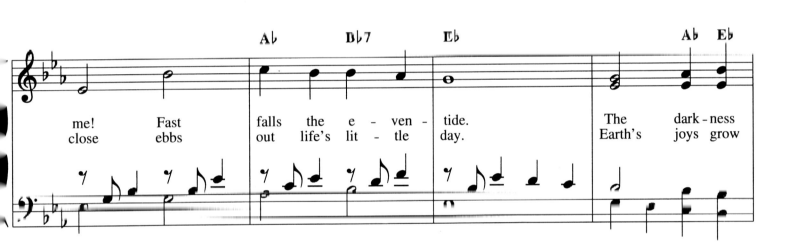

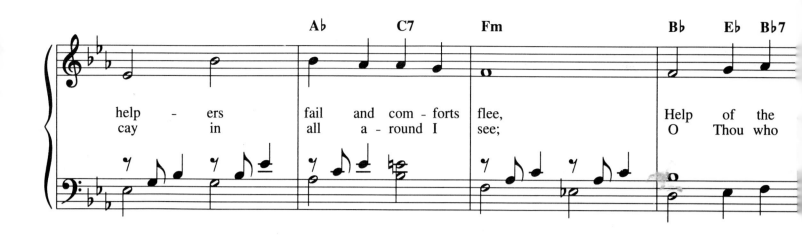

help - ers / cay   fail and com - forts / all a - round I   flee, / see;   Help of the / O Thou who

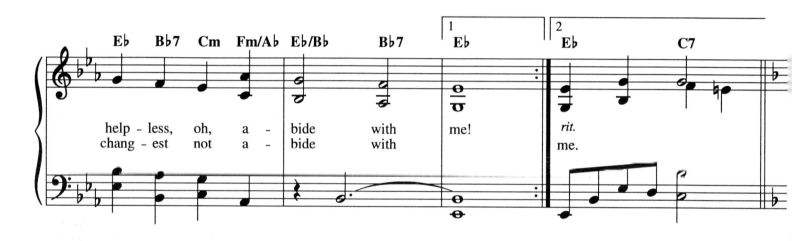

help - less, oh, a - / chang - est not a -   bide with   me! / me.   *rit.*

a tempo
I   need Thy   pres - ence   ev - 'ry pass - ing
I   fear no   foe with   Thee at hand to
(See additional verse)

hour. / bless;   What but Thy / Ills have no   grace can / weight, and   foil the tempt - er's / tears no bit - ter -

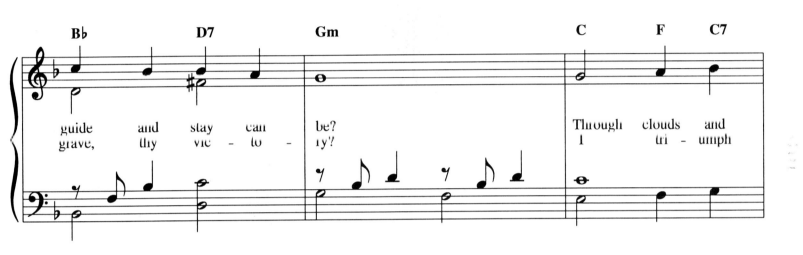

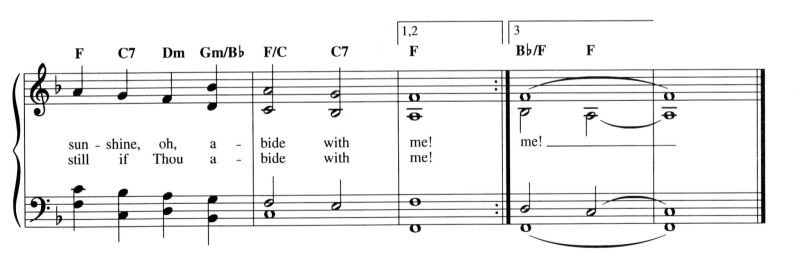

Additional Verse

(5.) Hold, Thou Thy cross before my closing eyes;
Shine through the gloom and point me to the skies.
Heav'n's morning breaks and earth's vain shadow flee!
In life, in death, O Lord, abide with me!

From the Hallmark Historical Collection. From an original 19th century greeting card published by Marcus Ward and Company, c. 1890s.

 LL GLORY, LAUD,
AND HONOR

The original Latin hymn, "Gloria, laus, et honor," was written by Theodulph, Bishop of Orleans, about 820, while he was imprisoned at Angers by King Louis I. It is thought that he secured his release from prison by singing this hymn from the window of his cell while the king was passing by. The anonymous tune ST. THEODULPH dates from a 1615 collection published at Leipzig.

ALL GLORY, LAUD, AND HONOR

Theodulph of Orleans, c. 820
tr. John Mason Neale, 1851

ST. THEODULPH
Melchior Teschner, 1615

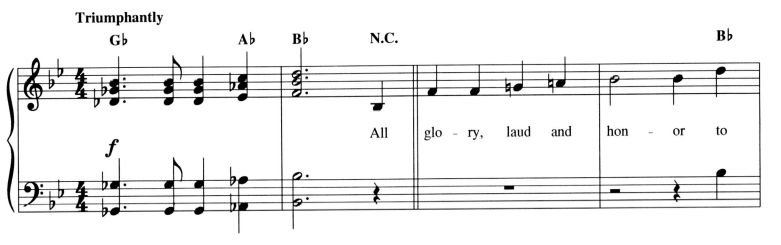

All glo-ry, laud and hon-or to

Thee, Re-deem-er, King, to whom the lips of chil-dren made

sweet ho-san-nas sing. Thou art the King of

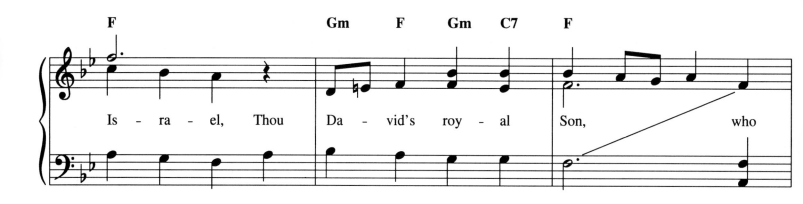

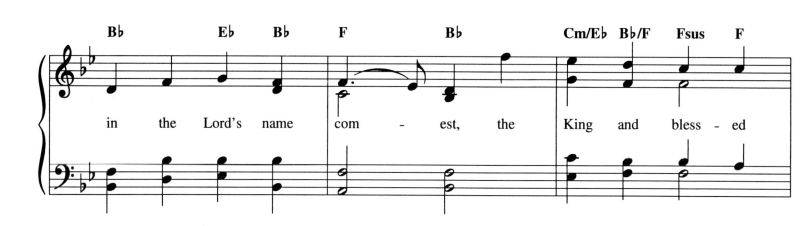

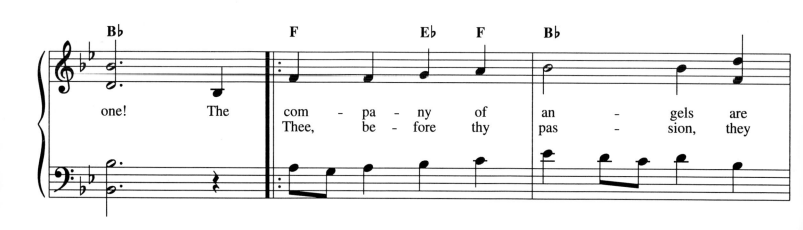

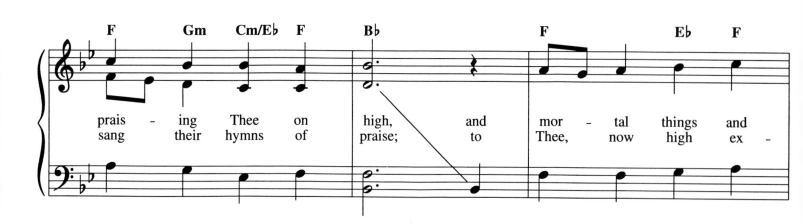

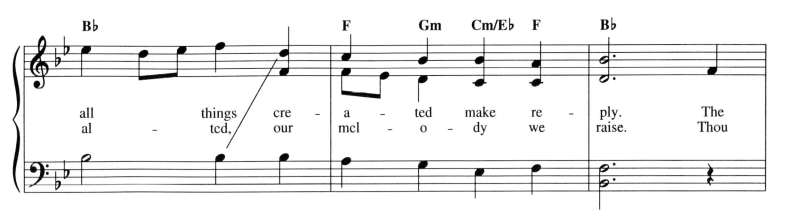

all things cre - a - ted make re - ply. The
al - tcd, our mcl - o - dy we raise. Thou

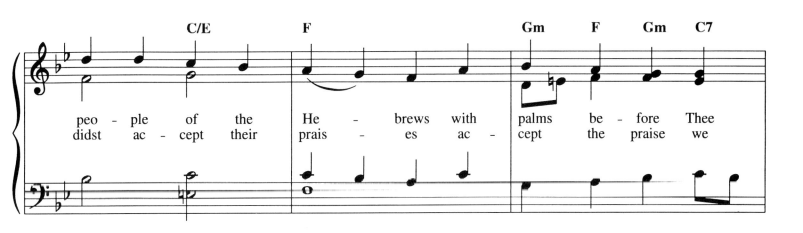

peo - ple of the He - brews with palms be - fore Thee
didst ac - cept their prais - es ac - cept the praise we

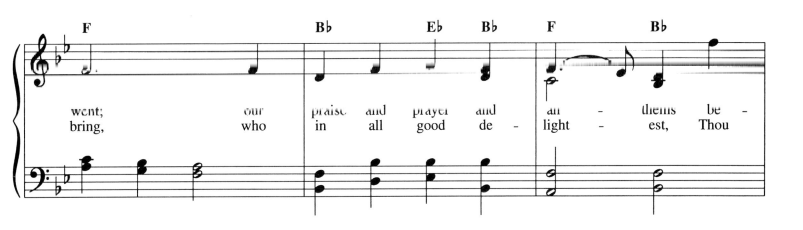

went; our praise and prayer and an - thems be -
bring, who in all good de - light - est, Thou

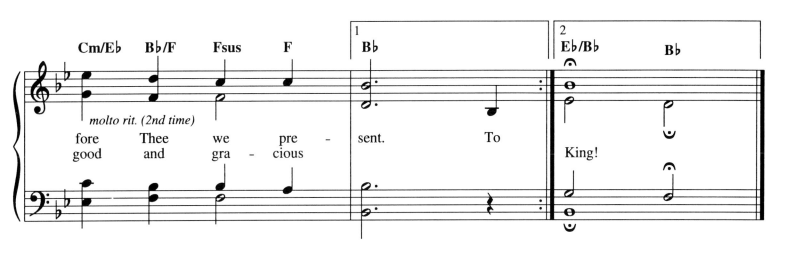

molto rit. (2nd time)

fore Thee we pre - sent. To
good and gra - cious

King!

"Let the Heavens rejoice, And let the Earth be glad!"

From the Hallmark Historical Collection. From an original 19th century greeting card published by Louis Prang of Boston.

ALL HAIL THE POWER OF JESUS' NAME

The initial stanza of Edward Perronet's hymn appeared in a religious periodical in November 1779. Five months later the complete eight stanzas appeared in the same periodical under the heading "On the Resurrection, the Lord Is King." Three hymn tunes are used for the hymn: MILES LANE, composed by English organist William Shrubsole in 1779; CORONATION, composed by American music teacher Oliver Holden in 1792; and DIADEM, composed by English musician James Ellor in 1838. Singing the hymn to any of these tunes is a thrilling experience.

ALL HAIL THE POWER OF JESUS' NAME

Edward Perronet, 1779
John Rippon, 1787

CORONATION
Oliver Holden, 1793

With strength

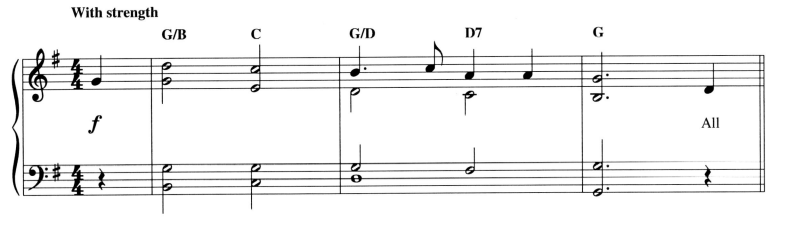

All

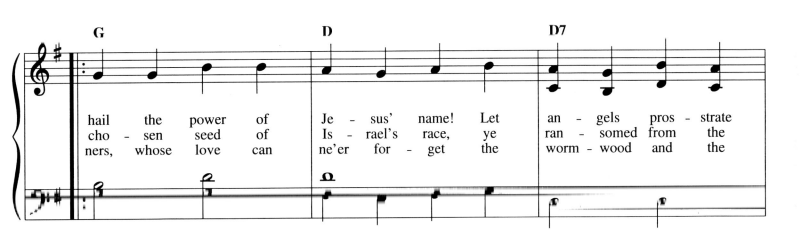

hail the power of Je - sus' name! Let an - gels pros - strate
cho - sen seed of Is - rael's race, ye ran - somed from the
ners, whose love can ne'er for - get the worm - wood and the

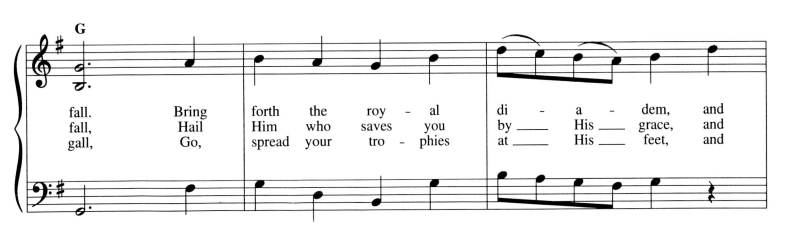

fall. Bring forth the roy - al di - a - dem, and
fall, Hail Him who saves you by ___ His ___ grace, and
gall, Go, spread your tro - phies at ___ His ___ feet, and

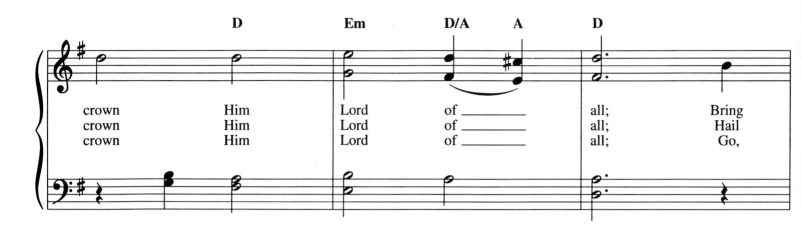

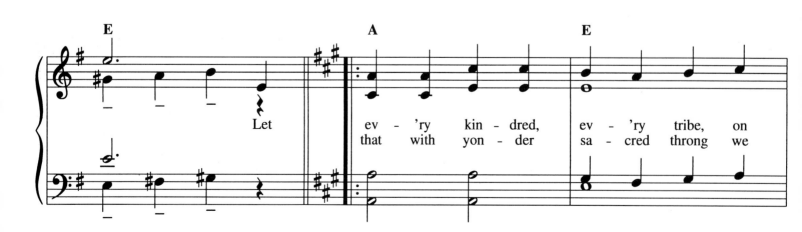

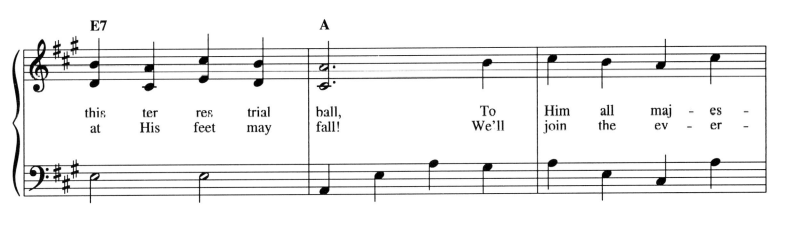

this ter res trial ball, To Him all maj - es -
at His feet may fall! We'll join the ev - er -

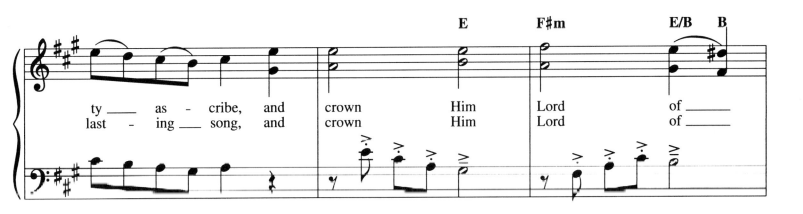

ty ___ as - cribe, and crown Him Lord of ___
last - ing ___ song, and crown Him Lord of ___

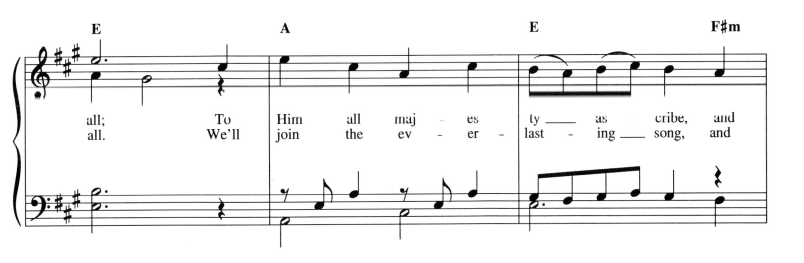

all; To Him all maj - es ty ___ as cribe, and
all. We'll join the ev - er - last - ing ___ song, and

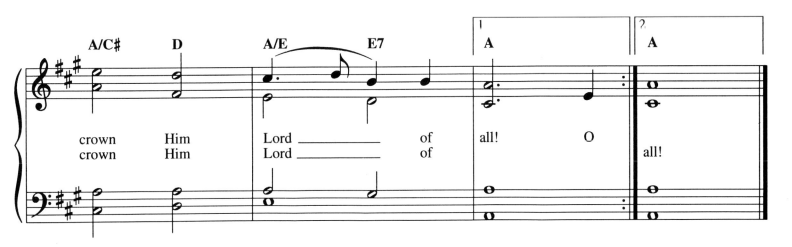

crown Him Lord _____ of all! O
crown Him Lord _____ of all!

MAZING GRACE

John Newton's hymn, in six four-line stanzas, appeared in his *Olney Hymns* (1779), a collection prepared for the evening Bible study classes in the village of Olney in Buckinghamshire, England. Newton, once a slave trader, had become a preacher of the divine grace "that saved a wretch like me." The musical setting of the hymn, NEW BRITAIN, is an American folk tune of unknown origin, dating from the early nineteenth century.

AMAZING GRACE

John Newton, 1779

NEW BRITAIN
Early 19th century

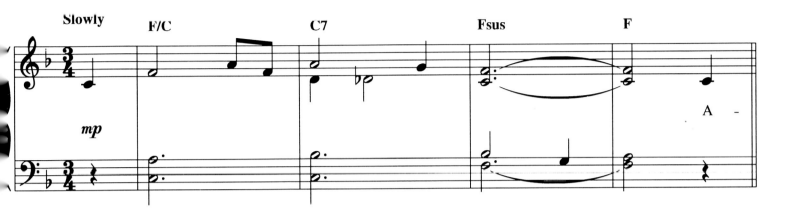

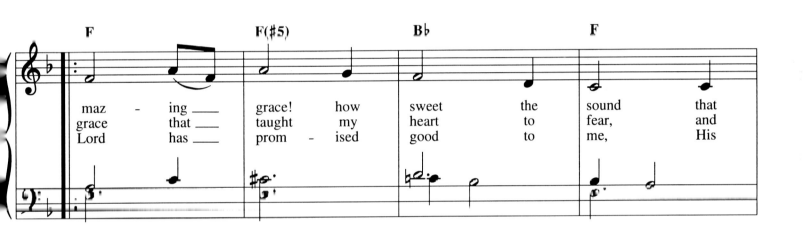

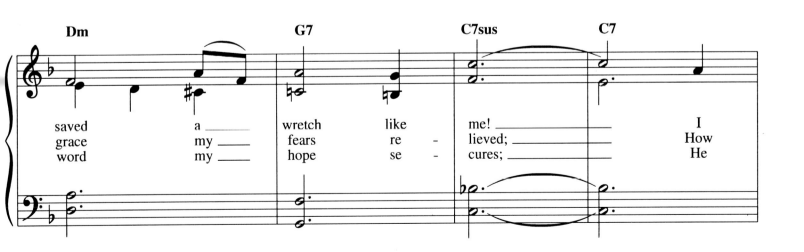

41

43

BE THOU MY VISION

The original ancient Irish poem dates from the eighth century. An English prose translation by Mary Byrne, a native of Dublin, was cast into a hymn by Eleanor Hull. SLANE is a traditional Irish air harmonized by David Evans for this text in 1927; Slane is a hill near Tara in County Meath where Patrick (c. 389–461), Ireland's patron saint, lit the paschal fire on Easter Eve, challenging King Loegaire and the Druid priests.

BE THOU MY VISION

Ancient Irish
tr. Mary Byrne, 1905
versified, Eleanor Hull, 1912

SLANE
Trad. Irish Melody

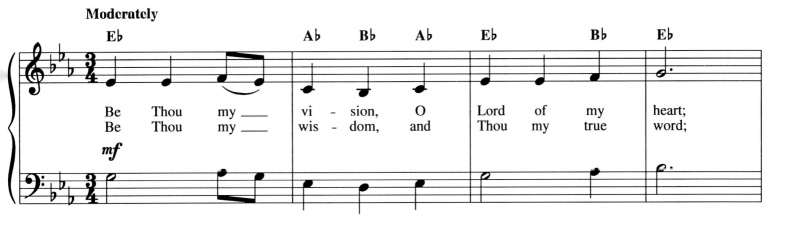

Be Thou my ____ vi - sion, O Lord of my heart;
Be Thou my ____ wis - dom, and Thou my true word;

naught be all else to me, save that Thou art;
I ev - er with Thee and Thou with me, Lord;

Thou my ____ best ____ thought, __ by day or by night, _____
Thou my ____ great ____ Fa - ther, I Thy true son, _____

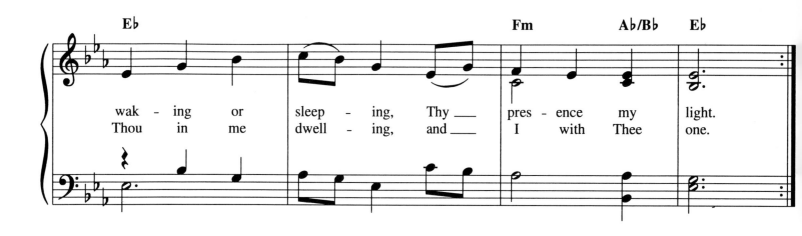

waking or sleeping, Thy — presence my light.
Thou in me dwelling, and — I with Thee one.

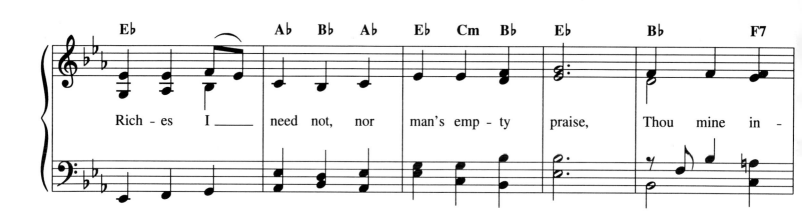

Rich - es I — need not, nor man's emp - ty praise, Thou mine in -

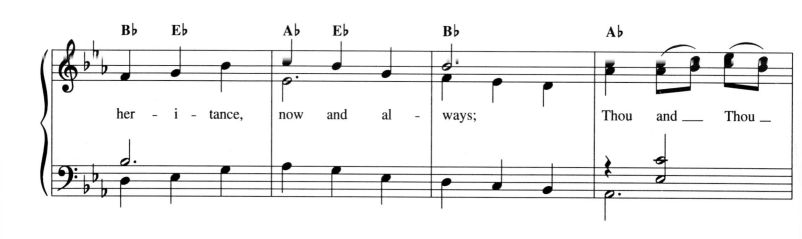

her - i - tance, now and al - ways; Thou and — Thou —

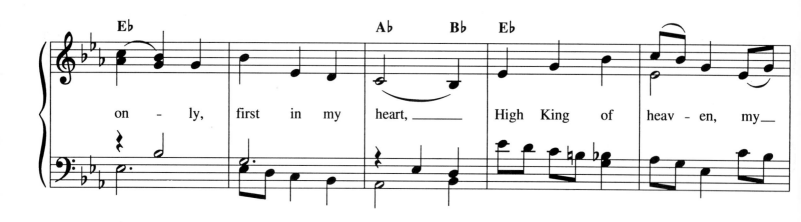

on - ly, first in my heart, — High King of heav - en, my —

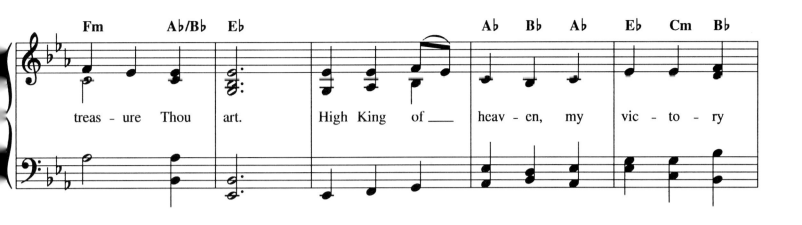

treas - ure Thou art. High King of ___ heav - en, my vic - to - ry

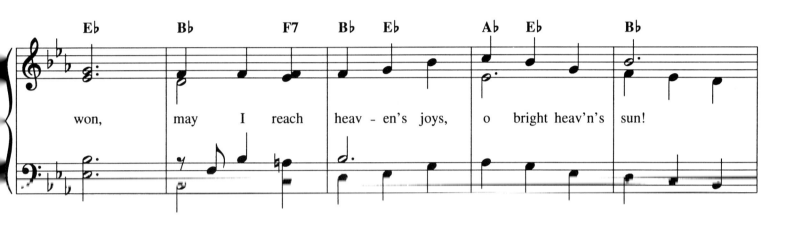

won, may I reach heav - en's joys, o bright heav'n's sun!

Heart of ___ my ___ own heart, what ev - er be - fall, ___

still be my vi - sion, O ___ Rul - er of all.

BLESSED ASSURANCE

In 1873, Fanny Crosby, the blind poet, visited Mrs. Joseph F. Knapp in her spacious apartment in the Savoy Hotel in New York City. Mrs. Knapp, wife of the founder of the Metropolitan Life Insurance Company, had written a new song. She played it for her friend and asked, "Fanny, what does that melody say to you?" Fanny Crosby replied, "Blessed assurance, Jesus is Mine." In a few minutes she had completed the stanzas and refrain. The song was published later that year.

BLESSED ASSURANCE

ASSURANCE
Phoebe Knapp, 1873

Fanny J. Crosby, 1873

Gently flowing

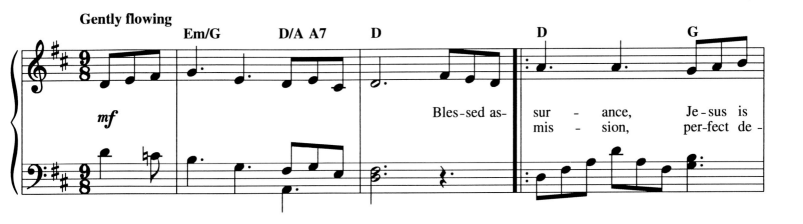

Bles-sed as- | sur - ance, | Je -sus is
mis - sion, | per-fect de -

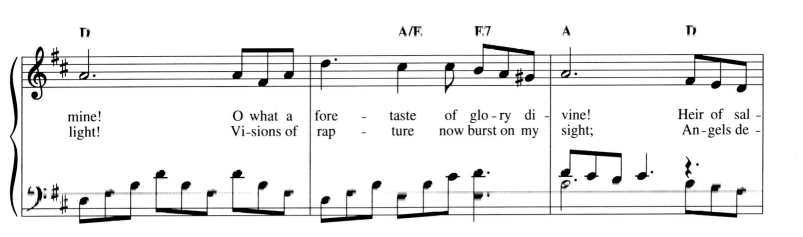

mine! | O what a | fore - taste | of glo-ry di - | vine! | Heir of sal -
light! | Vi-sions of | rap - ture | now burst on my | sight; | An -gels de -

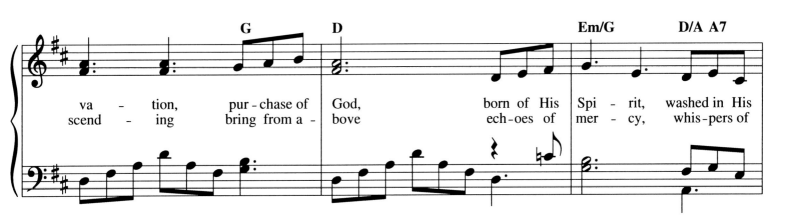

va - tion, | pur -chase of | God, | born of His | Spi - rit, | washed in His
scend - ing | bring from a - | bove | ech-oes of | mer - cy, | whis -pers of

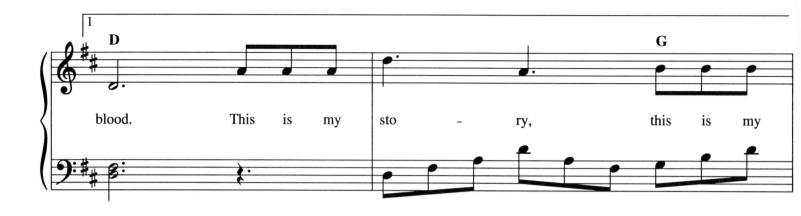

love.   This is my   sto - - - ry,   this is my

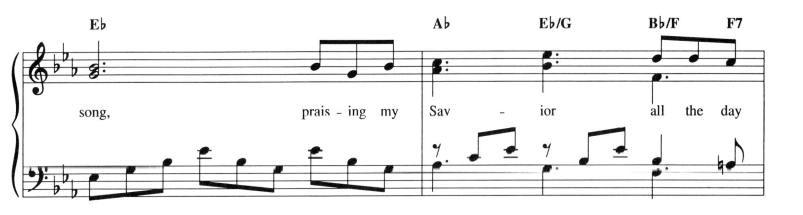

song,   prais - ing my Sav - - ior   all the day

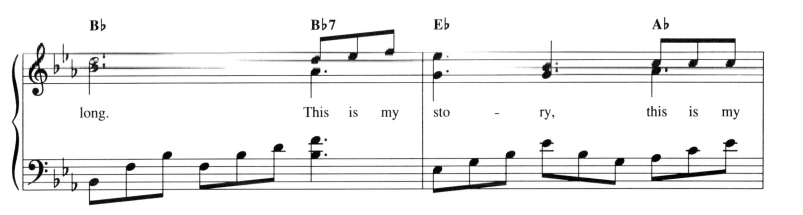

long.   This is my   sto - - ry,   this is my

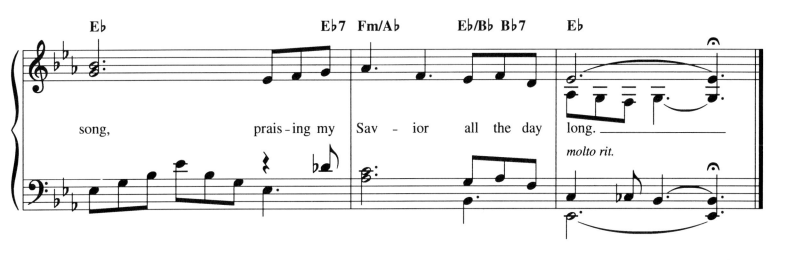

song,   prais - ing my Sav - ior all the day long. _____

molto rit.

CHRIST THE LORD IS RISEN TODAY

Charles Wesley's joyous hymn celebrating the resurrection of Christ was written in 1739. No doubt Wesley patterned the hymn after the translation of a fourteenth-century Easter carol, "Surrexit Christus hodie," which added a jubilant "Alleluia" to each line of the stanza. The exuberant hymn tune EASTER HYMN is of unknown origin, and dates from an English collection published in 1708. The tune reflects the purposes set forth in the preface of this collection by the editors that they wished "for a little freer air than the grand movements of the psalm-tunes." Their objective was nobly achieved.

CHRIST THE LORD IS RISEN TODAY

Charles Wesley, 1739

EASTER HYMN
Lyra Davidica, 1708

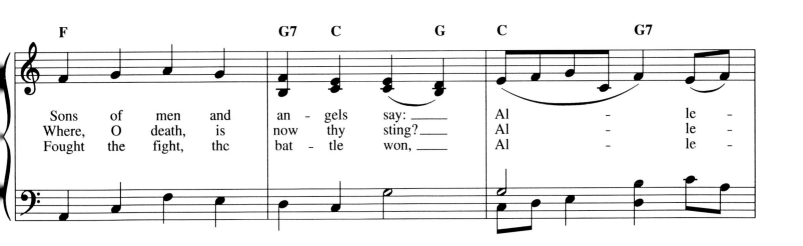

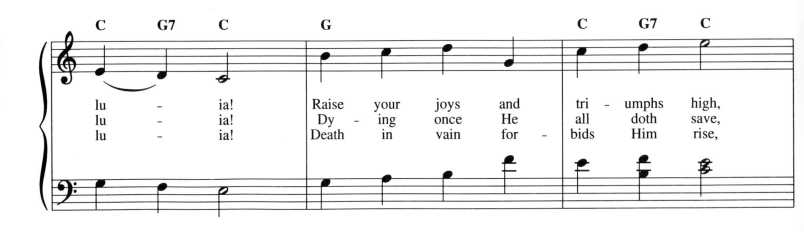

lu - ia! Raise your joys and tri - umphs high,
lu - ia! Dy - ing once He all doth save,
lu - ia! Death in vain for - bids Him rise,

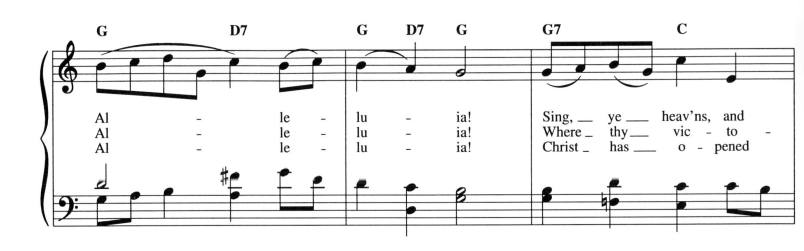

Al - le - lu - ia! Sing, __ ye __ heav'ns, and
Al - le - lu - ia! Where _ thy __ vic - to -
Al - le - lu - ia! Christ _ has __ o - pened

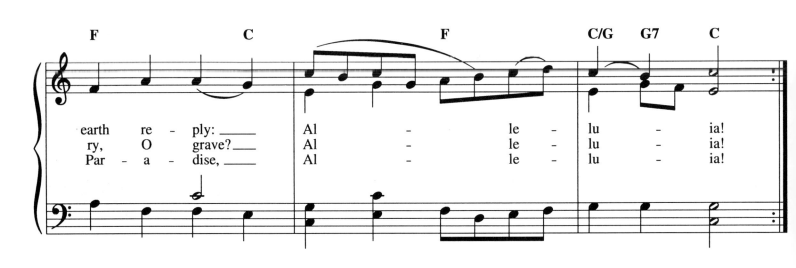

earth re - ply: ____ Al - le - lu - ia!
ry, O grave? ____ Al - le - lu - ia!
Par - a - dise, ____ Al - le - lu - ia!

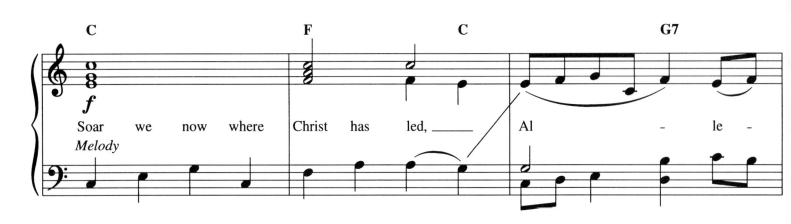

Soar we now where Christ has led, ____ Al - le -
Melody

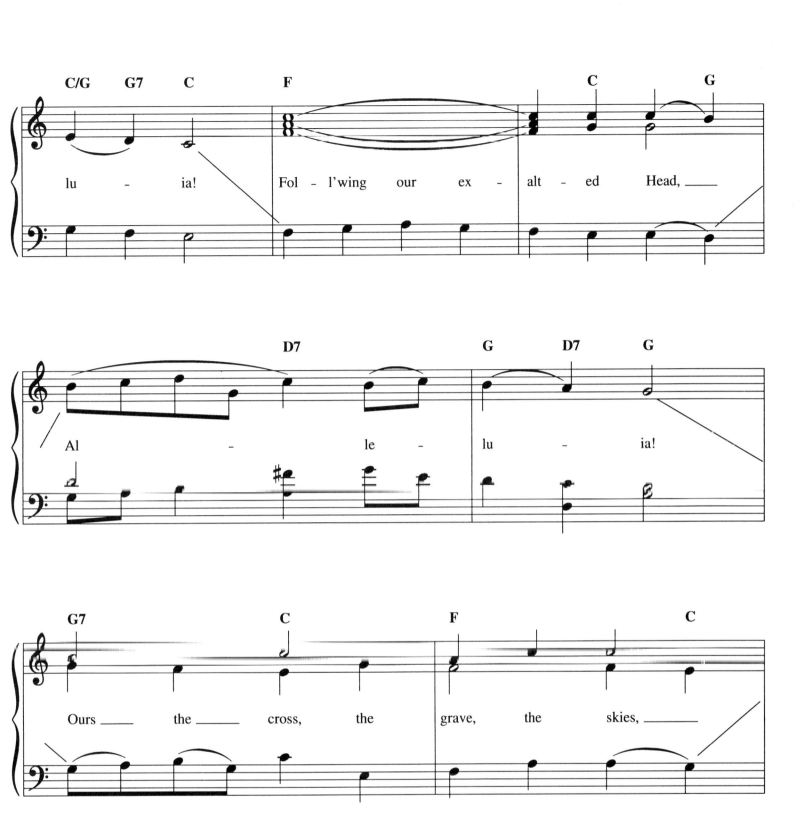

lu - ia! Fol - l'wing our ex - alt - ed Head, ____

Al - le - lu - ia!

Ours ____ the ____ cross, the grave, the skies, ____

Al - le - lu - ia!

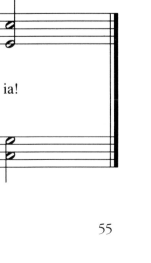

55

From the Hallmark Historical Collection. From an original 19th century greeting card published by De La Rue & Co., 1880-1890.

COME, THOU ALMIGHTY KING

The anonymous hymn dates from 1757, and is thought to have been sung in England to the tune of "God Save the King." During the American Revolution, a detachment of British soldiers surprised worshippers in a church service on Long Island, New York, one Sunday morning. The British officer ordered the startled congregation to stand and sing "God Save the King." The congregation obeyed by singing heartily the right tune but substituting the words "Come, Thou Almighty King." ITALIAN HYMN, the tune so long associated with this text, was composed by Felice de Giardini, an Italian musician who lived in London.

COME, THOU ALMIGHTY KING

ITALIAN HYMN
Felice de Giardini, 1769

Anon., 1757

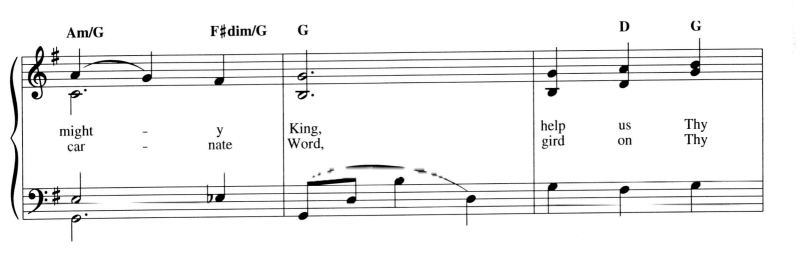

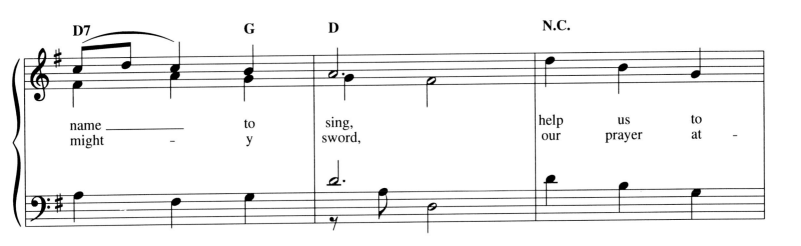

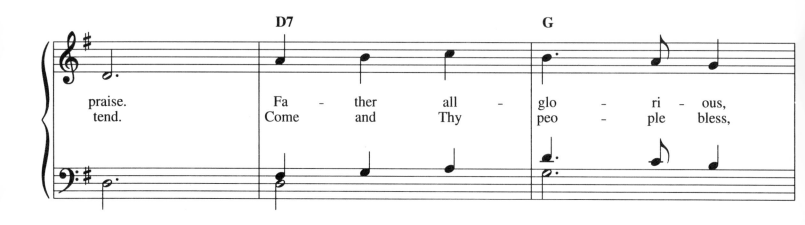

praise.
tend.

Fa - ther all - glo - ri - ous,
Come and all Thy peo - ple bless,

o'er all vic - to - ri - ous,
and all give Thy word suc - cess,

come and reign
Spir - it reign of

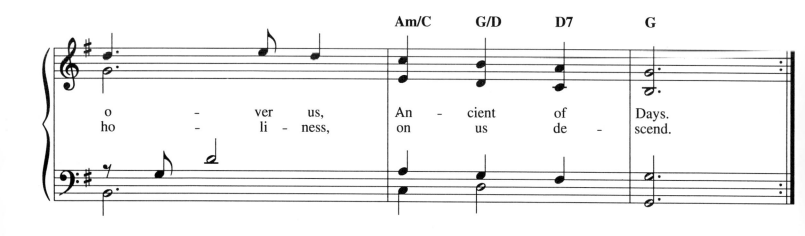

o - ver us,
ho - li - ness,

An - cient of Days.
on us de - scend.

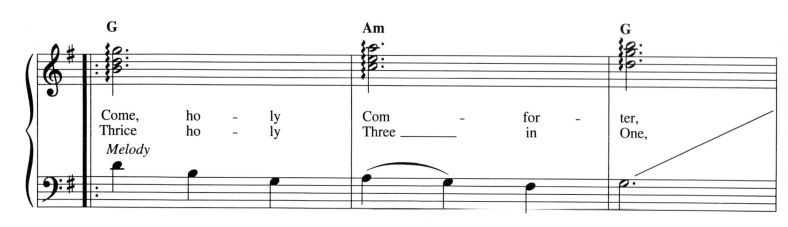

Come, ho - ly Com - for - ter,
Thrice ho - ly Three ____ in One,

Melody

58

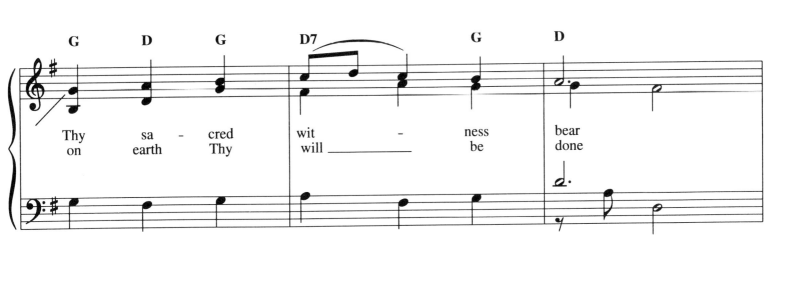

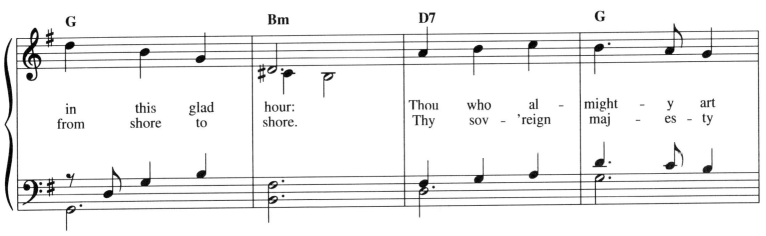

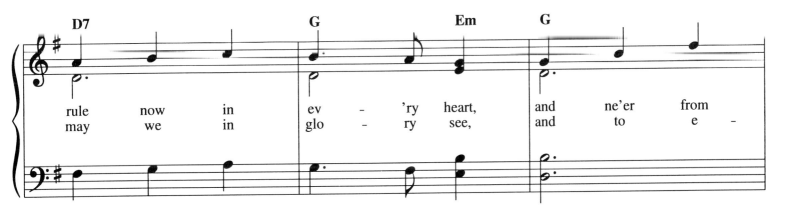

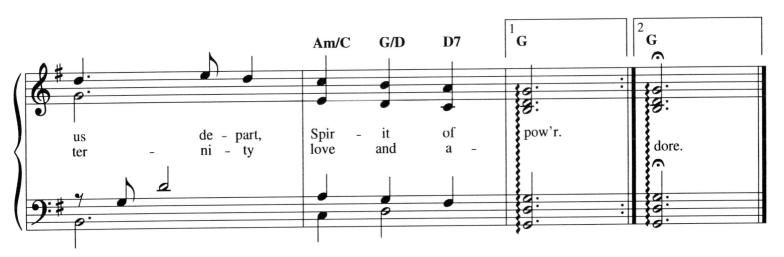

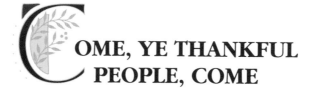

OME, YE THANKFUL PEOPLE, COME

Henry Alford, Church of England minister, wrote the hymn in 1844. A distinguished clergyman, he became dean of Canterbury Cathedral in 1857. The hymn begins with an invitation to thankful people to express their gratitude to God for his bountiful goodness. George J. Elvey's tune ST. GEORGE'S WINDSOR provides an expressive setting for the hymn. For 47 years Elvey served as organist at St. George's Chapel, Windsor. Windsor Castle, once of the English royal residences, dates from the eleventh century.

COME, YE THANKFUL PEOPLE, COME

Henry Alford, 1844

ST. GEORGE'S WINDSOR
George J. Elvey, 1858

Come, ye thank-ful peo-ple, come,
All the world is God's own field,

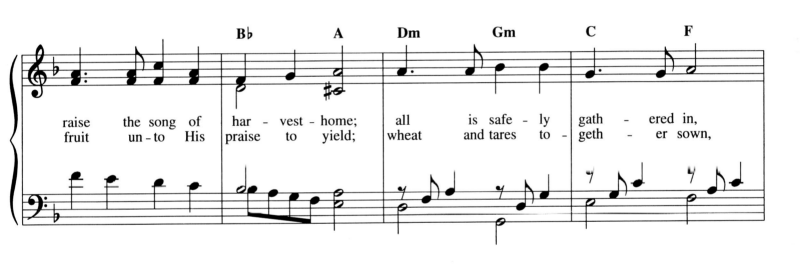

raise the song of har-vest-home; all is safe-ly gath-ered in,
fruit un-to His praise to yield; wheat and tares to-geth-er sown,

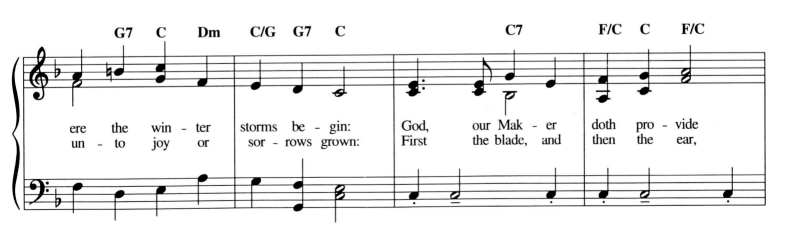

ere the win-ter storms be-gin: God, our Mak-er doth pro-vide
un-to joy or sor-rows grown: First the blade, and then the ear,

for our wants to be sup - plied;
then the full corn shall ap - pear;
come to God's own
Lord of har - vest,

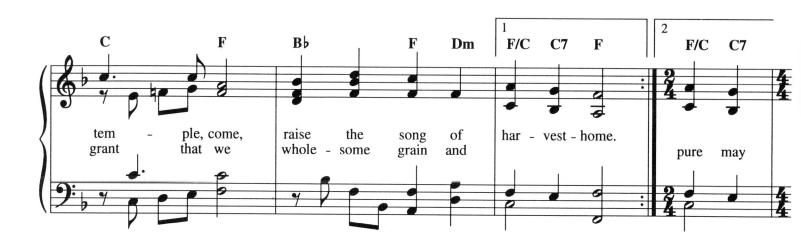

tem - ple, come,
grant that we
raise the song of
whole - some grain and
har - vest - home.
pure may

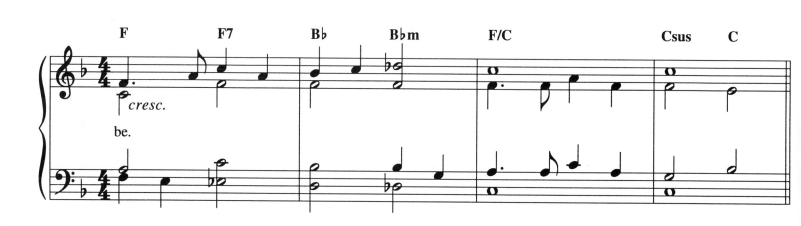

cresc.
be.

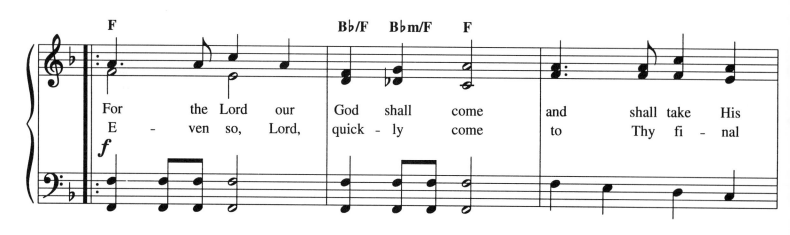

For the Lord our God shall come and shall take His
E - ven so, Lord, quick - ly come to Thy fi - nal

f

From the Hallmark Historical Collection. *From an original 19th century greeting card published by Campbell & Tudhope.*

ETERNAL FATHER, STRONG TO SAVE

William Whiting, master of the Winchester College Choristers' School, wrote the words in 1860 for a student who was leaving for America. The following year John B. Dykes composed the tune, which he named MELITA, for the place where the apostle Paul was shipwrecked (Acts 28:1). The hymn is known as the "Navy Hymn." A favorite of Franklin D. Roosevelt, it was sung at his funeral at Hyde Park, New York, April 14, 1945. As the body of John Fitzgerald Kennedy was borne up the steps of the Capitol Building in Washington on November 23, 1963, the hymn was played by the Navy band. At the conclusion of the burial service at Arlington National Cemetery the next day, it was played by the Marine band.

ETERNAL FATHER, STRONG TO SAVE

William Whiting, 1860

MELITA
John B. Dykes, 1861

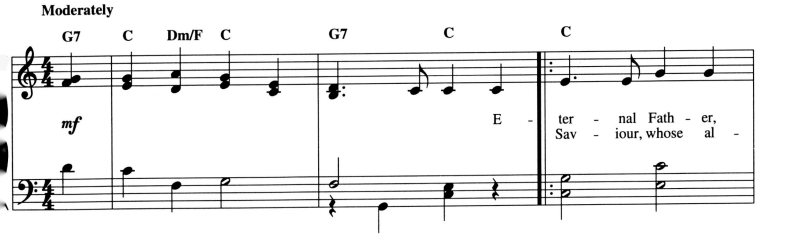

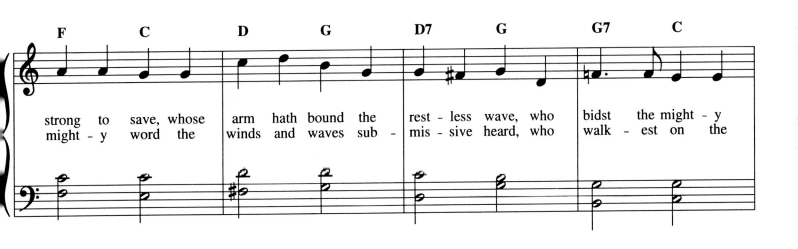

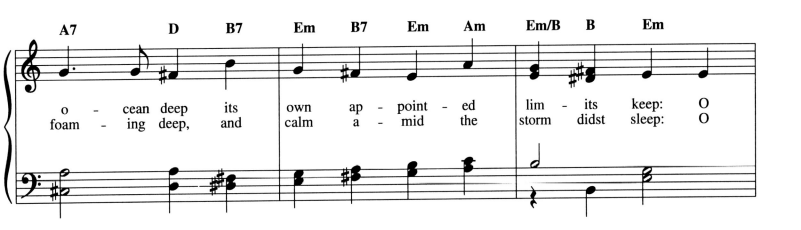

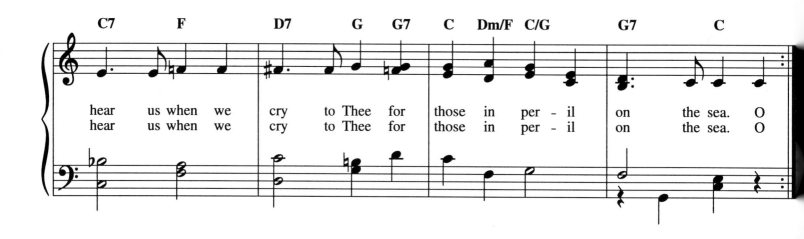

hear us when we cry to Thee for those in per - il on the sea. O
hear us when we cry to Thee for those in per - il on the sea. O

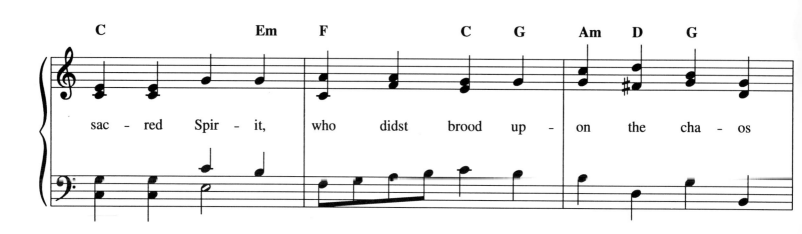

sac - red Spir - it, who didst brood up - on the cha - os

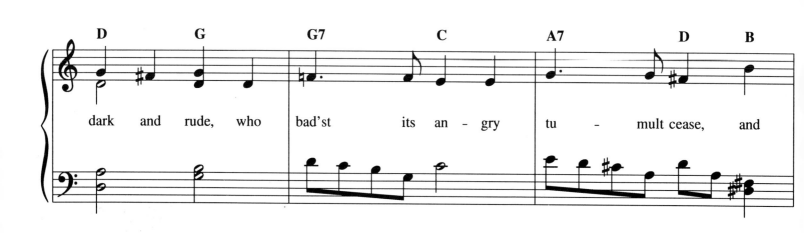

dark and rude, who bad'st its an - gry tu - mult cease, and

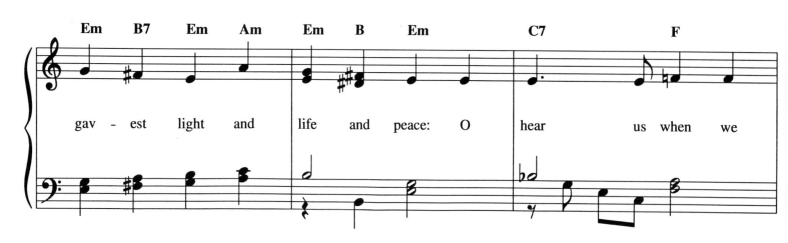

gav - est light and life and peace: O hear us when we

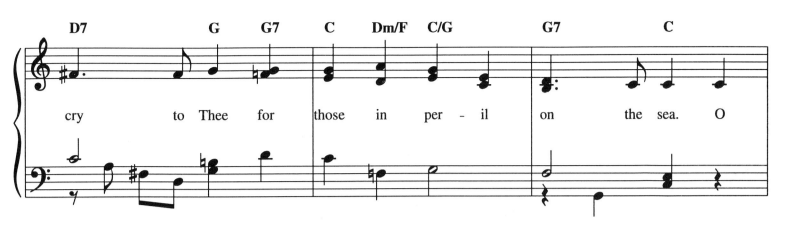

cry to Thee for those in per - il on the sea. O

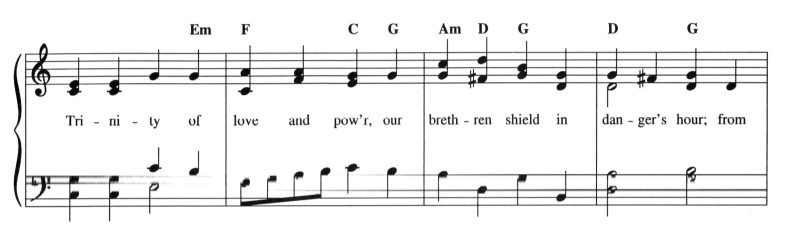

Tri - ni - ty of love and pow'r, our breth - ren shield in dan - ger's hour; from

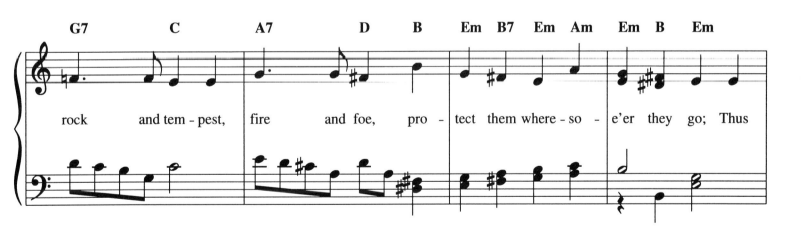

rock and tem - pest, fire and foe, pro - tect them where - so - e'er they go; Thus

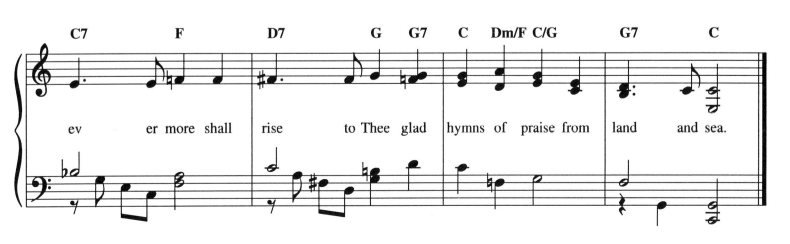

ev - er more shall rise to Thee glad hymns of praise from land and sea.

I AM THE LIGHT OF THE WORLD

© Hallmark Cards, Inc.

FAIREST LORD JESUS
(Beautiful Savior)

An imagined, romantic story associates the hymn with the Holy Crusades of centuries ago. Though the story is wholly untrue, little is known about the actual origin of the words and music. The German text, "Schönster Herr Jesu," has been traced to the Jesuits in Münster, Westphalia, Germany, in the seventeenth century. The hymn tune, CRUSADERS' HYMN, is based on a Silesian folk song from Leipzig. The hymn reminds us that regardless of how beautiful are the meadows, the woodlands, the flowers of spring, the sun and stars, Jesus is fairer and brighter, even "purer than all the angels heaven can boast."

FAIREST LORD JESUS
(BEAUTIFUL SAVIOR)

Anon. German, *Münster Gesangbuch,* 1677
tr. Anon., 1850
st. 4, Joseph A. Seiss, 1873

CRUSADERS' HYMN
Schlesische Volkslieder, 1842
arr. Richard S. Willis, 1850

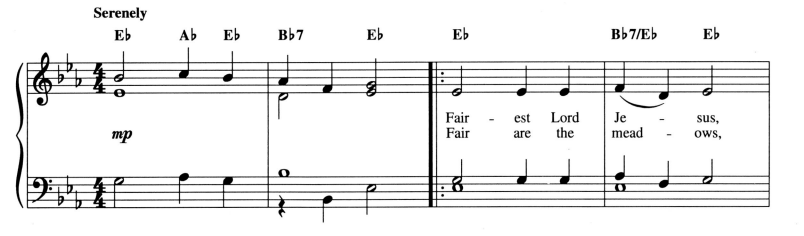

Fair - est Lord Je - sus,
Fair are the mead - ows,

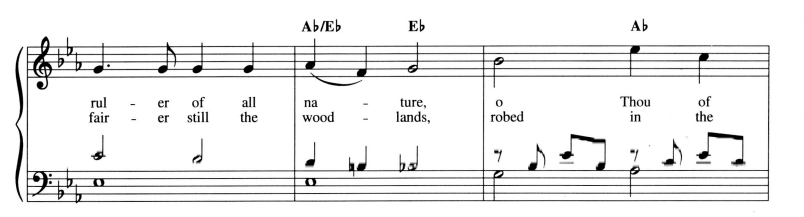

rul - er of all na - ture, o robed Thou of
fair - er still the wood - lands, garb in the

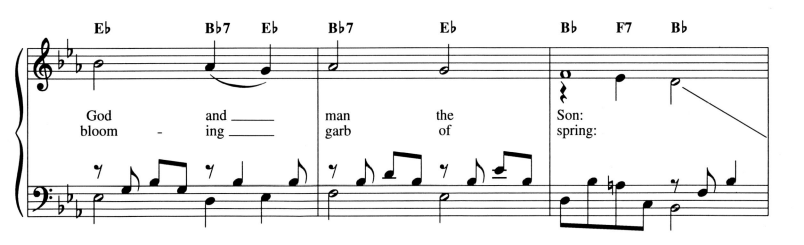

God and _____ man the Son:
bloom - ing _____ garb of spring:

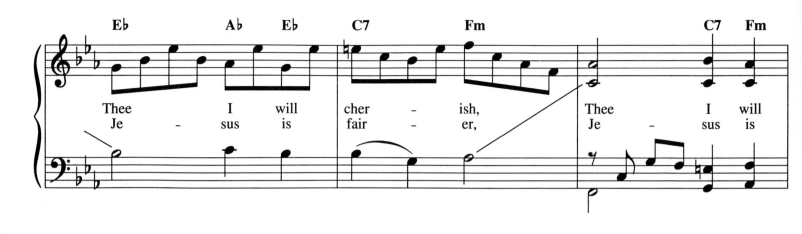

Thee I will cher - ish,
Je - sus is fair - er,

hon - or, Thou my soul's glo - ry, joy, and
pur - er, who makes the woe - ful

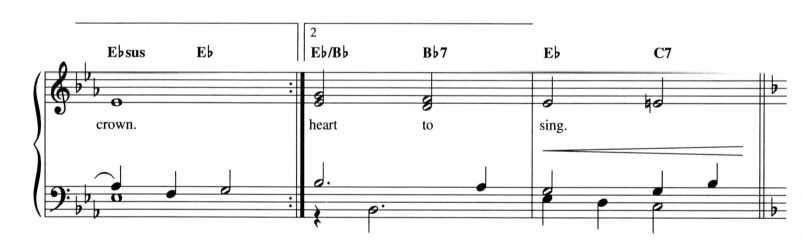

crown.
heart to sing.

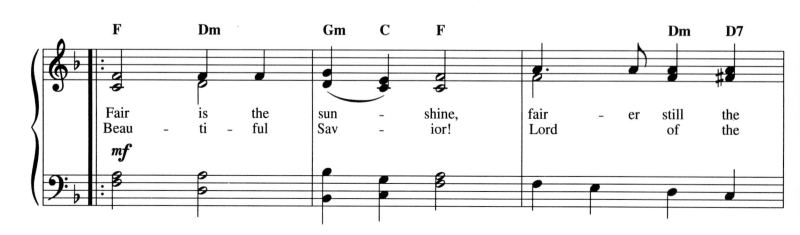

Fair is the sun - shine, fair - er still the
Beau - ti - ful Sav - ior! Lord of the

71

Be joyful
in hope,
patient in
affliction,
faithful in
prayer.

ROMANS 12:12

FAITH OF OUR FATHERS

Frederick W. Faber's hymn was published in London in 1849. The Christian faith described in Hebrews 11 provided the inspiration for the hymn. The pages of Christian history bear the names of many martyrs who refused to deny their faith. Some were crucified, some beheaded, some burned at the stake, or otherwise brutally killed. Because of their faith in Christ, they made secure for us the rich heritage of a living faith "in spite of dungeon, fire, and sword." ST. CATHERINE, composed by Henri F. Hemy, was named for Catherine of Alexandria, a fourth-century Christian martyr.

FAITH OF OUR FATHERS

ST. CATHERINE
Henri F. Hemy, 1864
arr. James G. Walton, 1874

Frederick W. Faber, 1849

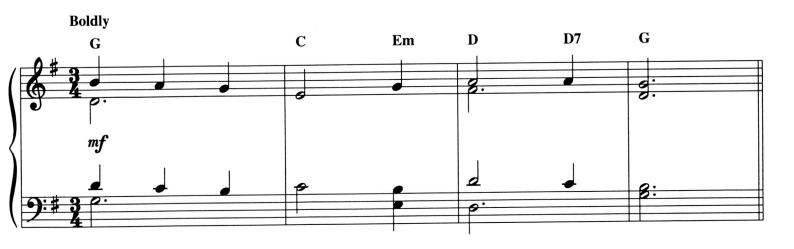

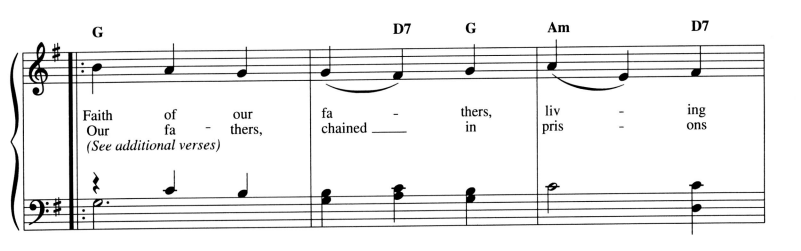

Faith of our fa — thers, living
Our fa — thers, chained ____ in pris — ons

(See additional verses)

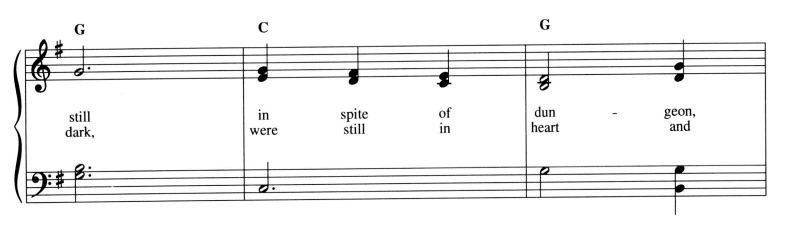

still in spite of dun — geon, and
dark, were still in heart

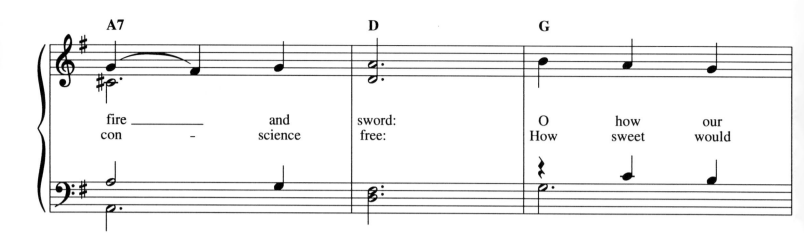

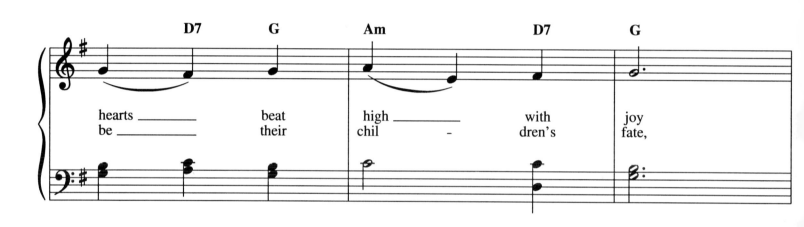

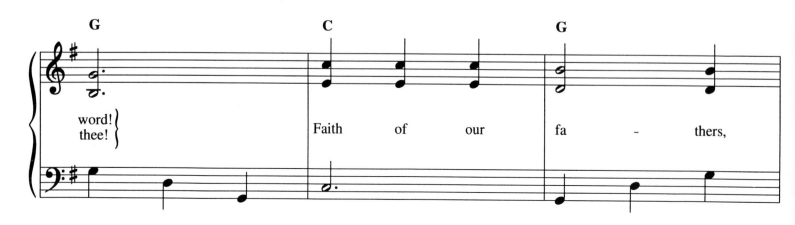

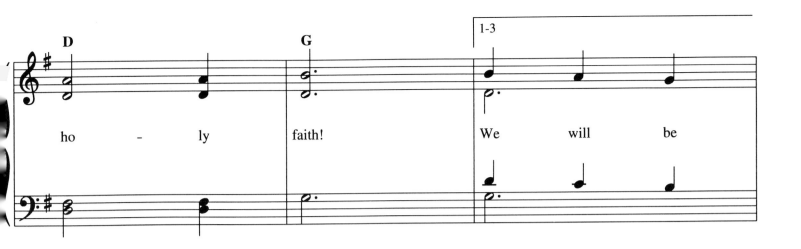

ho - ly faith! We will be

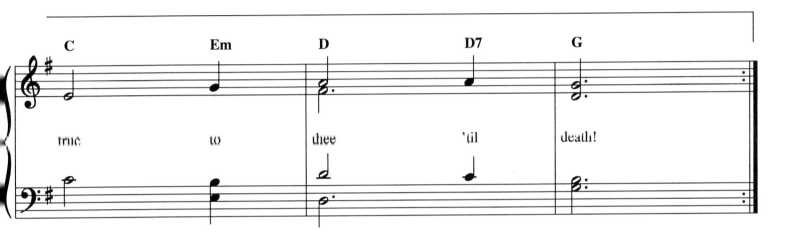

true to thee 'til death!

We will be true to thee 'til death!

Additional Verses

3. Faith of our fathers! we will strive to win all nations unto Thee,
   And thro' the truth that comes from God, mankind shall then be truly free.

4. Faith of our fathers! we will love both friend and foe in all our strife:
   And preach thee too as love knows how, by kindly words and virtuous life:

And those who know thy name put their trust in thee,
for thou, O Lord,
hast not forsaken those who seek thee.
PSALM 9:10

GOD BE WITH YOU TILL WE MEET AGAIN

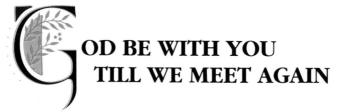

The familiar expression "goodbye" is a contraction of "God be with you." Jeremiah E. Rankin wrote the hymn as a "Christian goodbye" for the First Congregational Church, Washington, D.C., where he served as minister for 15 years. He requested that his friend William G. Tomer compose a musical setting, and the hymn was published in 1880. Some hymnals use the tune RANDOLPH, composed by Ralph Vaughan Williams in 1906.

GOD BE WITH YOU TILL WE MEET AGAIN

Jeremiah E. Rankin, 1880

GOD BE WITH YOU
William G. Tomer, 1880

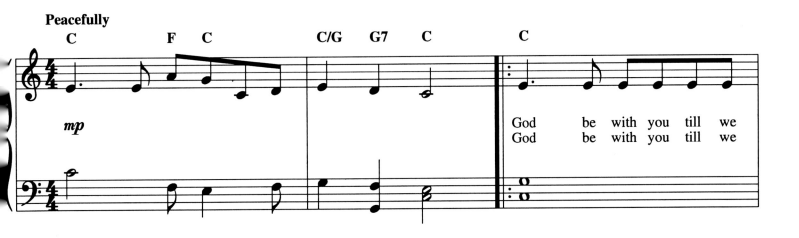

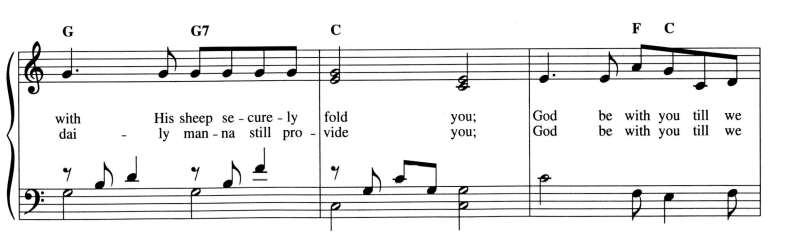

meet a - gain. } Till we meet, _____ till we meet, _____ till we
meet a - gain.

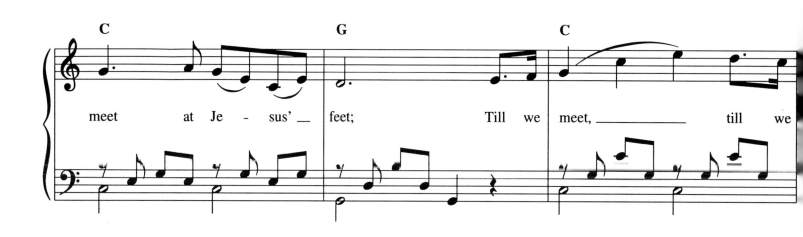

meet at Je - sus' _ feet; Till we meet, _____ till we

meet, _____ God be with you till we meet a - gain.

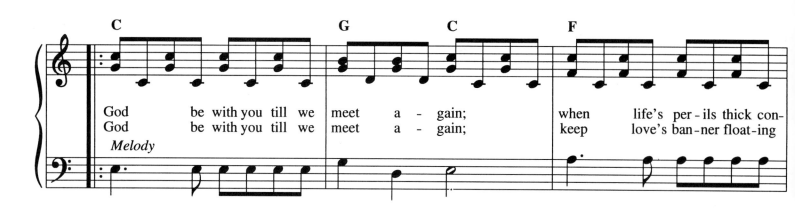

God be with you till we meet a - gain; when life's per - ils thick con-
God be with you till we meet a - gain; keep love's ban - ner float-ing

Melody

found you, / o'er you, | put / smite His arms un-fail-ing / death's threat-'ning wave be- 'round / fore you; / you;

God be with you till we meet a-gain. } Till we meet, ____ till we

meet, ____ till we meet at Je - sus' ___ feet; Till we

meet, ____ till we meet, ____ God be with you till we meet a - gain.

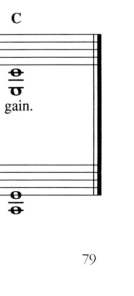

GOD OF OUR FATHERS

For the centennial celebration of the Fourth of July, Daniel C. Roberts wrote this hymn in 1876. He was rector of St. Thomas Episcopal Church, Brandon, Vermont. Later George W. Warren, organist at St. Thomas' Church, New York City, composed the tune NATIONAL HYMN for the hymn to be sung at the centennial celebration of the United States Constitution. Expressing gratitude for God's help in the past, the hymn prays for God's blessing in the present and also in the future.

GOD OF OUR FATHERS

Daniel C. Roberts, 1876

NATIONAL HYMN
George W. Warren, 1888

God of our fa - thers,
Thy love di - vine hath

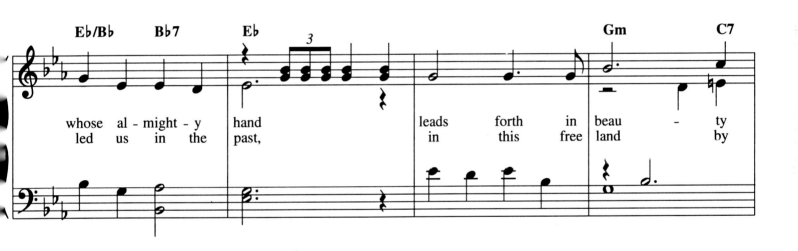

whose al - might - y hand leads forth in beau - ty
led us in the past, in this free land by

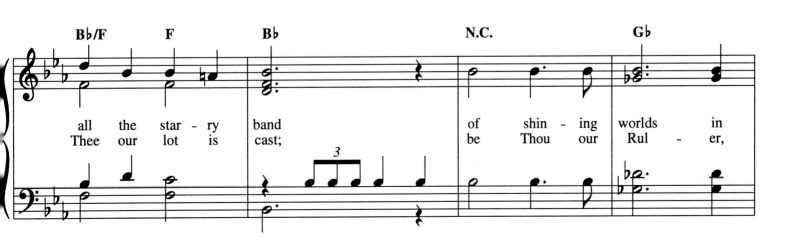

all the star - ry band of shin - ing worlds in
Thee our lot is cast; be Thou our Rul - er,

splen - dor through the skies,   our   grate - ful songs be -
Guard - ian, Guide and Stay,   Thy   word our law, be Thy

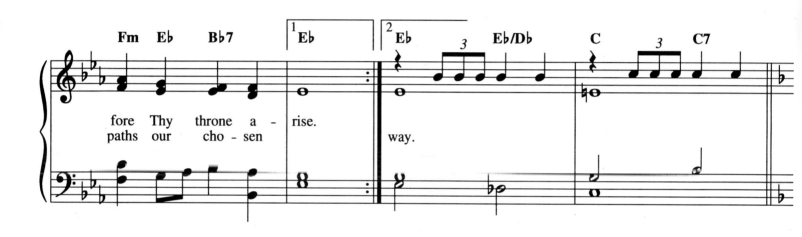

fore Thy throne a - rise.
paths our   cho - sen   way.

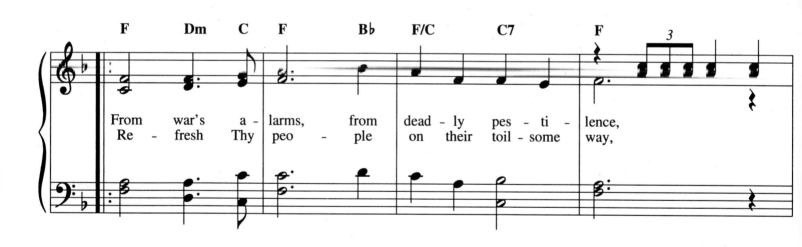

From war's a - larms,   from dead - ly pes - ti - lence,
Re - fresh Thy peo - ple on their toil - some way,

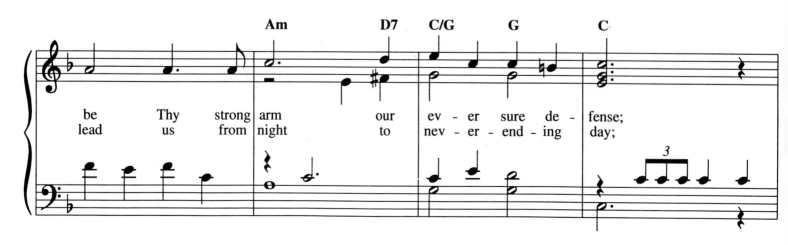

be   Thy strong arm   our   ev - er sure de - fense;
lead us from night   to   nev - er - end - ing day;

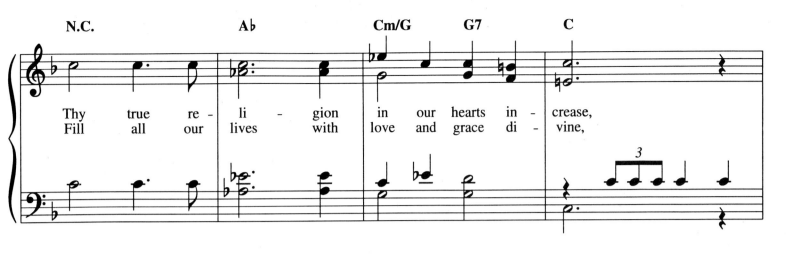

Thy true re - li - gion in our hearts in - crease,
Fill all our lives with love and grace di - vine,

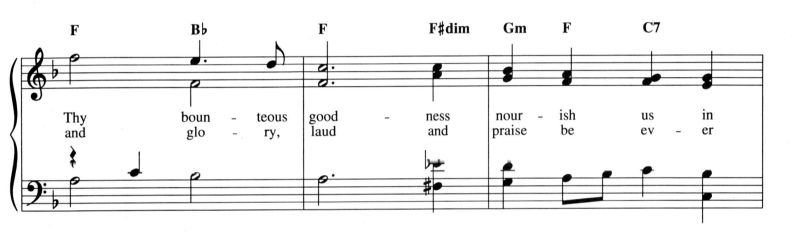

Thy boun - teous good - ness nour - ish us in
and glo - ry, laud and praise be ev - er

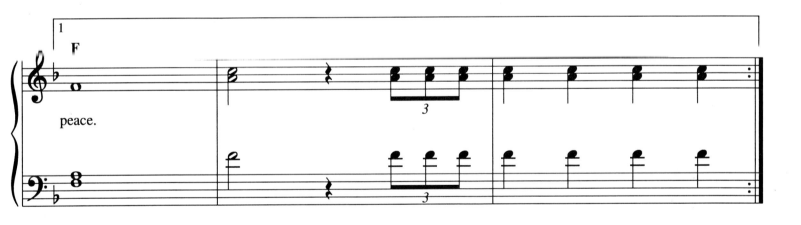

peace.

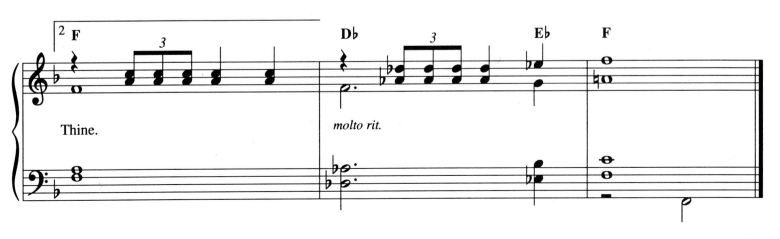

Thine.

molto rit.

HAVE THINE OWN WAY, LORD

Adelaide Pollard, while attending a prayer meeting, heard someone lead in prayer, saying, "Lord, just have your own way with us." The words lingered in her mind, and that evening at home she wrote the four stanzas. Later the words were given to George C. Stebbins, noted gospel song composer, and he provided the tune now known as ADELAIDE, and the hymn was published in 1907.

HAVE THINE OWN WAY, LORD

Adelaide A. Pollard, 1907

ADELAIDE
George C. Stebbins, 1907

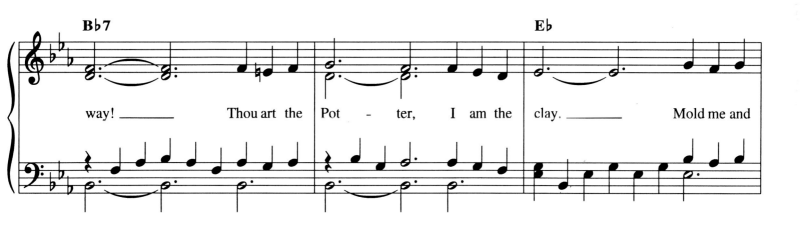

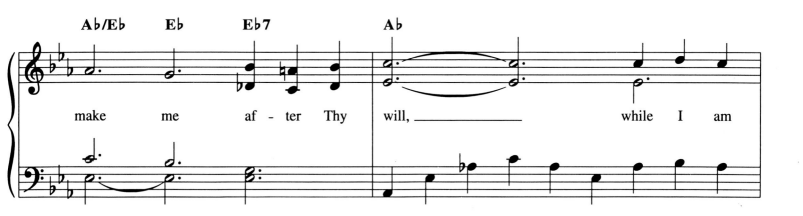

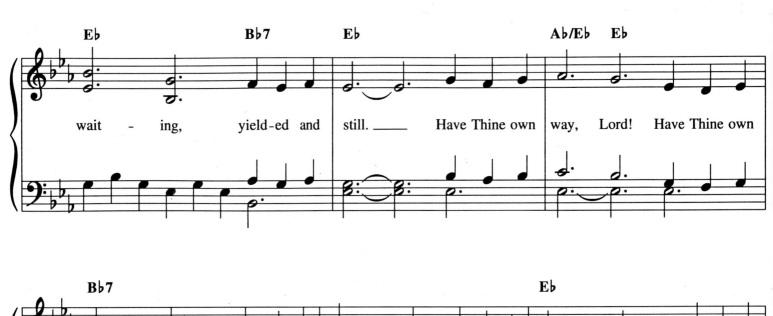

waiting, yield-ed and still. _____ Have Thine own way, Lord! Have Thine own

way! _____ Search me and try me, Mas-ter, to-day! _____ Whit-er than

snow, Lord, wash me just now, _____ as in Thy

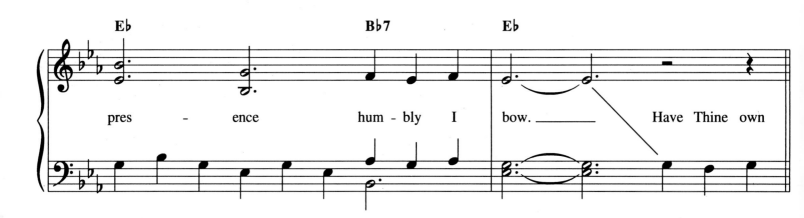

pres - ence hum-bly I bow. _____ Have Thine own

"HE LEADETH ME BESIDE THE STILL WATERS"

From the Hallmark Historical Collection. From an original 19th century greeting card published by De La Rue & Co., 1880-1890.

HE LEADETH ME

Joseph H. Gilmore, a young theology student, was the supply preacher at the First Baptist Church, Philadelphia. His sermon on Wednesday evening, March 26, 1861, was based on Psalm 23. He discussed the subject further after the service with Deacon Wattson, in whose home he was staying. After retiring for the evening, Gilmore penciled the stanzas of "He Leadeth Me" on the back of his sermon notes. Three years later these stanzas, set to music composed by William B. Bradbury, were published in New York.

HE LEADETH ME

Joseph H. Gilmore, 1862

HE LEADETH ME
William B. Bradbury, 1864

Moderately

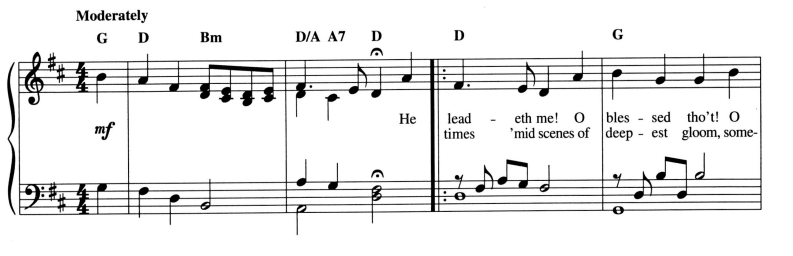

He lead - eth me! O bles - sed tho't! O
times 'mid scenes of deep - est gloom, some-

words with heav'n - ly ___ com - fort fraught! What-e'er I do, wher - e'er I be, still ___
times where E - den's _ bow - ers blooms by wa - ters still, o'er troub - led sea, still ___

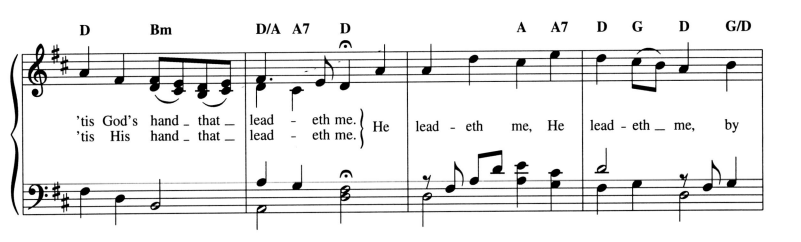

'tis God's hand _ that _ lead - eth me. } He lead - eth me, He lead - eth _ me, by
'tis His hand _ that _ lead - eth me.

His own hand __ He __ lead - eth me: His faith - ful fol - lower

I would __ be, for by His hand __ He __ lead - eth me. Some-

lead - eth me. Lord, | I could clasp Thy hand in mine, nor
when my task on earth is done, when,

ev - er mur - mur __ nor re - pine, con - tent, what - ev - er
by Thy grace, the __ vic - t'ry's won, e'en death's cold wave I

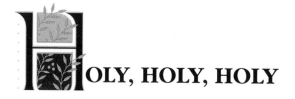

From the Hallmark Historical Collection.
From an original 19th century greeting card
published by Marcus Ward & Company.

HOLY, HOLY, HOLY

Reginald Heber, a Church of England minister, became rector
of his father's church in the small village of Hodnet in western
England. He wrote "Holy, Holy, Holy" for his congregation to sing
on Trinity Sunday. John B. Dykes composed the tune NICAEA for
Heber's hymn in 1861 and named it for the Council of Nicaea,
A.D. 325, which affirmed the Christian doctrine of the Trinity
God the Father, God the Son, and God the Holy Spirit.

HOLY, HOLY, HOLY

Reginald Heber, 1826

NICAEA
John B. Dykes, 1861

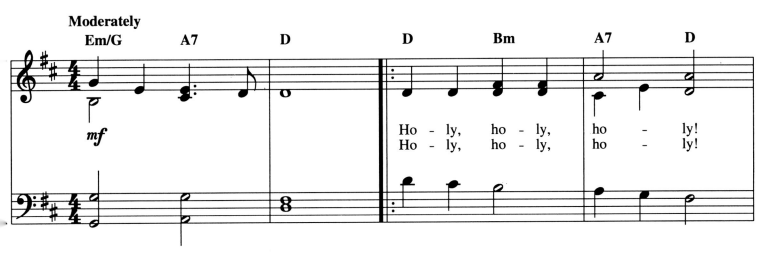

Ho - ly, ho - ly, ho - ly!
Ho - ly, ho - ly, ho - ly!

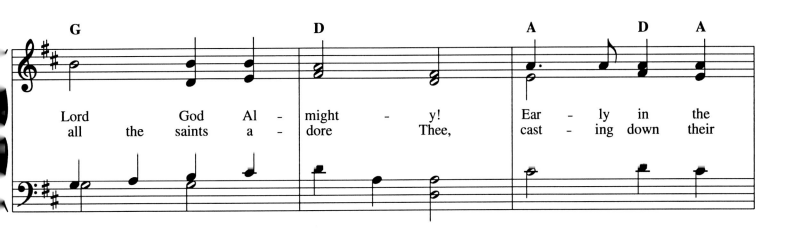

Lord   God Al - might   - y!   Ear - ly in the
all the saints a - dore   Thee,   cast - ing down their

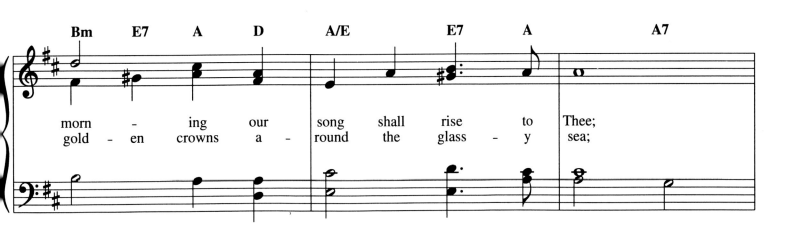

morn   -   ing   our   song   shall   rise   to   Thee;
gold - en   crowns   a - round   the   glass - y   sea;

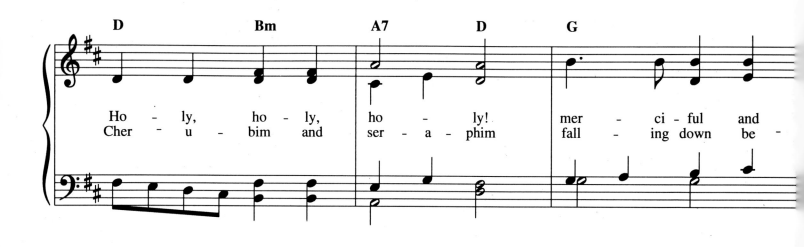

Ho - ly, ho - ly, ho - ly! mer - ci - ful and
Cher - u - bim and ser - a - phim fall - ing down be -

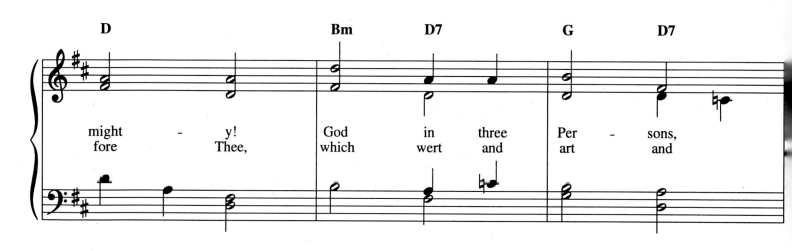

might - y! God which in three Per - sons,
fore Thee, which wert and art and

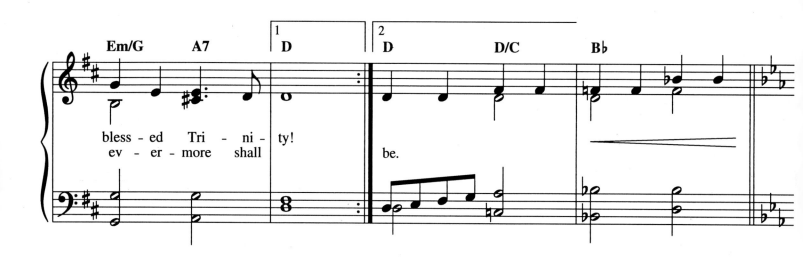

bless - ed Tri - ni - ty!
ev - er - more shall be.

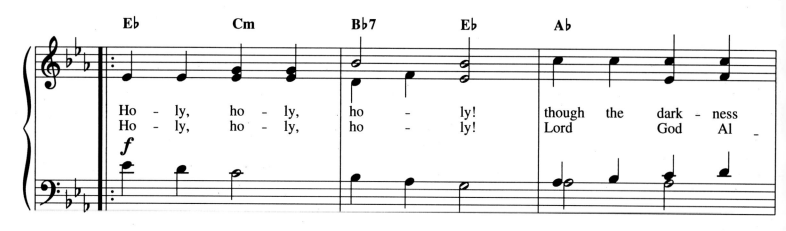

Ho - ly, ho - ly, ho - ly! though the dark - ness
Ho - ly, ho - ly, ho - ly! Lord God Al -

hide Thee, though the eye of sin - ful man Thy
might - y! All Thy works shall praise Thy name in

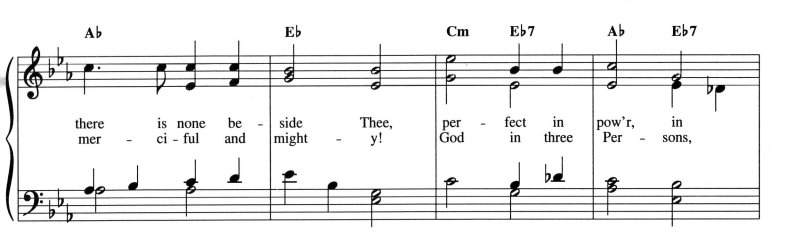

glo - ry may not see; On - ly Thou art ho - ly —
earth and sky and sea; Ho - ly, ho - ly, ho - ly!

there is none be - side Thee, per - fect in pow'r, in
mer - ci - ful and might - y! God in three Per - sons,

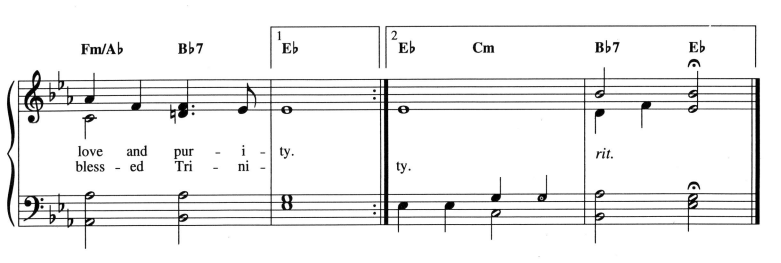

love and pur - i - ty. ty.
bless - ed Tri - ni - ty.

rit.

From the Hallmark Historical Collection. From an original 19th century chromolithography.

HOW FIRM A FOUNDATION

This hymn of unknown origin first appeared in 1787, in a hymnal published by John Rippon, the foremost Baptist minister of his day in England. The hymn tune, also of unknown origin, first appeared in a shape-note tunebook published in 1832 in the Shenandoah Valley of Virginia. The compiler, Joseph Funk, a devout Mennonite, worked as a farmer, a printer, and a singing-school teacher. The hymn was a favorite of Andrew Jackson's. He requested that it be sung by his family and friends at the Hermitage as he was dying, "as an expression of his full trust in the ways of the Heavenly Father."

HOW FIRM A FOUNDATION

Anon., 1787

FOUNDATION
Joseph Funk's *Genuine Harmony*, 1832

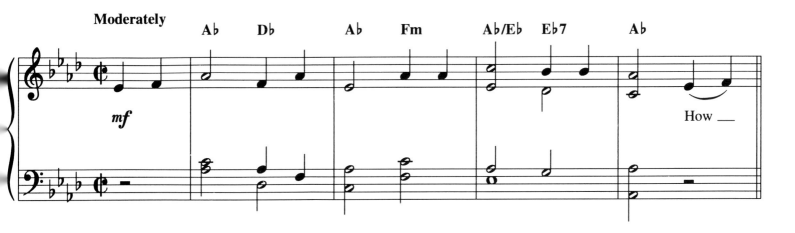

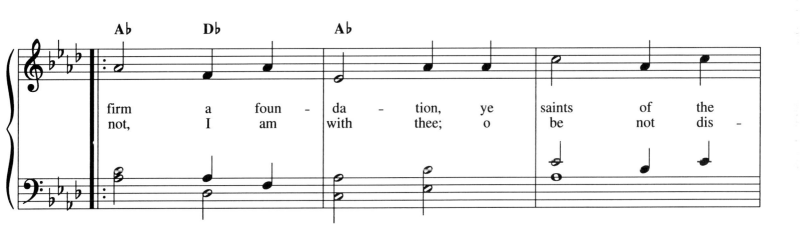

firm   a   foun   -   da   -   tion,   ye   saints   of   the
not,   I   am   with   thee;   o   be   not   dis -

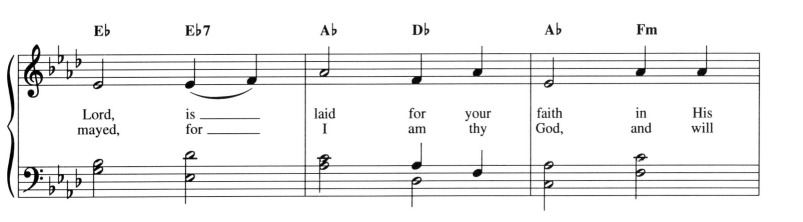

Lord,   is ____   laid   for   your   faith   in   His
mayed,   for ____   I   am   thy   God,   and   will

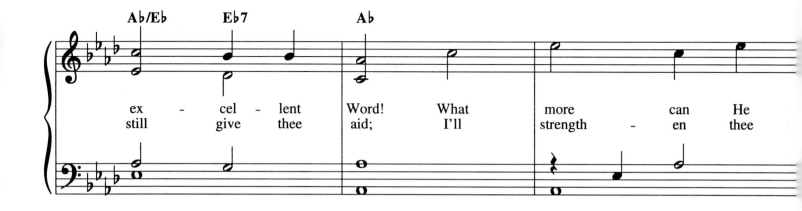

ex - cel - lent Word! What more can He
still give thee aid; I'll strength - en He thee

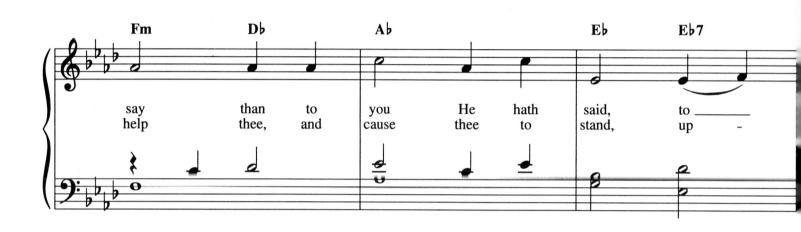

say than to you He hath said, to ___
help thee, and cause thee to stand, up -

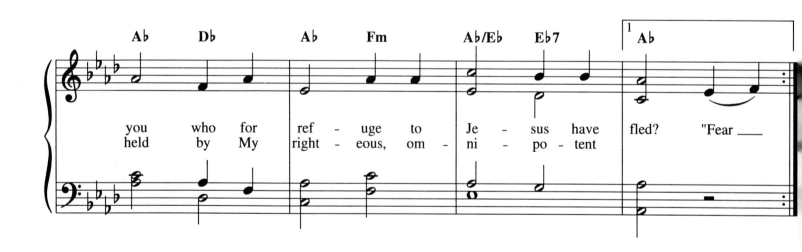

you who for ref - uge to Je - sus have fled? "Fear ___
held by My right - eous, om - ni - po - tent

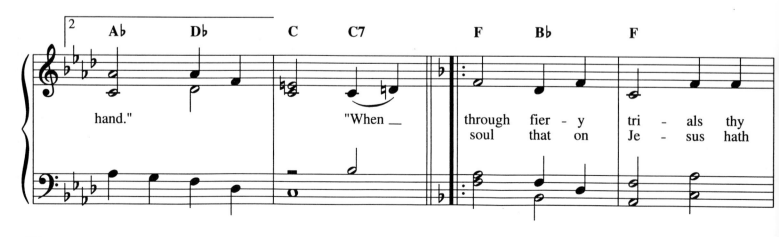

hand." "When ___
soul that on Je - sus hath

through fier - y tri - als thy

98

path - way shall | lie, My ____ | grace, all suf - | fi - cient, shall
learned for re - | pose I ____ | will not, I | will not de -

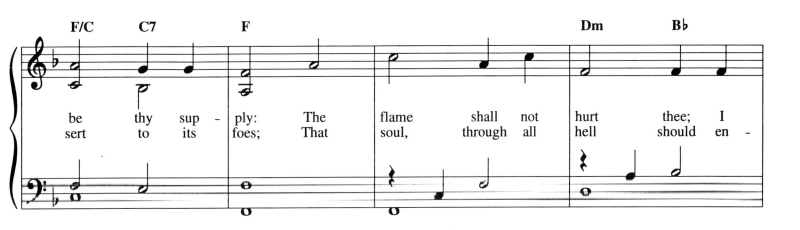

be thy sup - | ply: The | flame shall not | hurt thee; I
sert to its | foes; That | soul, through all | hell should en -

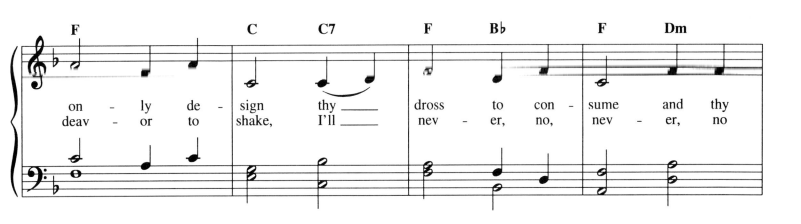

on - ly de - | sign thy ____ | dross to con - | sume and thy
deav - or to | shake, I'll ____ | nev - er, no, | nev - er, no

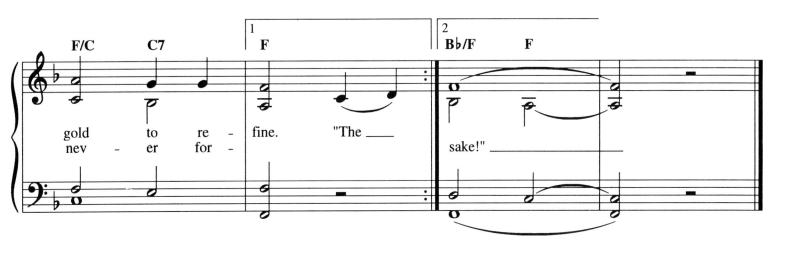

gold to re - | fine. "The ____ |
nev - er for - |

1. F
2. B♭/F F

sake!" ____

From the Hallmark Historical Collection. From an original 19th century greeting card published by Louis Prang of Boston.

HOW GREAT THOU ART

Carl Boberg, editor of a Swedish Christian newspaper, wrote the original Swedish hymn in 1886, and set it to the Swedish folk tune O STORE GUD. Translated into German, then into Russian, it was discovered by Stuart K. Hine, a Methodist missionary to the Ukraine. He translated the first stanza, and later added the other stanzas. George Beverly Shea and Cliff Barrows introduced it in the meetings of the Billy Graham Crusade in Toronto in 1955. Now the world knows and sings it.

HOW GREAT THOU ART

Carl Boberg, 1886
tr. Stuart K. Hine, 1949

O STORE GUD
Swedish Folk Melody, 1891

O Lord my God, whom I in awe - some
woods and for - est glades I
think that God, His Son not

won - der _____ Con - sid - er all the worlds Thy hands have made, I see the
wan - der _____ And hear the birds sing sweet - ly in the trees, When I look
spar - ing, _____ Sent Him to die, I scarce can take it in, That on the

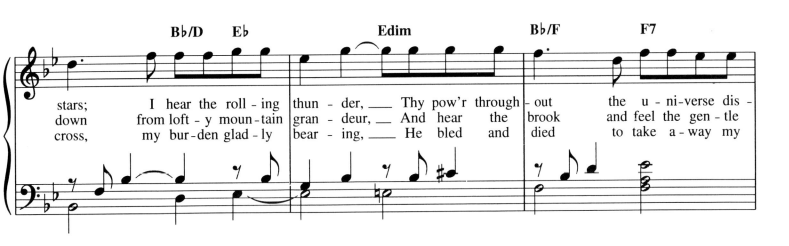

stars; I hear the roll - ing thun - der, _____ Thy pow'r through - out the u - ni-verse dis -
down from loft - y moun - tain gran - deur, _____ And hear the brook and feel the gen - tle
cross, my bur - den glad - ly bear - ing, _____ He bled and died to take a - way my

From the Hallmark Historical Collection. From an original 19th century card, c. 1890s.

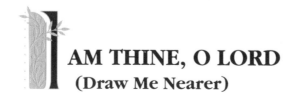

I AM THINE, O LORD
(Draw Me Nearer)

Fanny J. Crosby wrote the hymn during a visit to the home of William Doane in Cincinnati, Ohio. Their extended conversation about the nearness of God one evening provided the inspiration. In the quietness of her room before she retired, she wrote the text of the hymn based on Hebrews 10:22: "Let us draw near with a true heart." Doane, a successful businessman, composed the music, and the song was published in 1875.

I AM THINE, O LORD
(DRAW ME NEARER)

Fanny J. Crosby, 1875

I AM THINE
William H. Doane, 1875

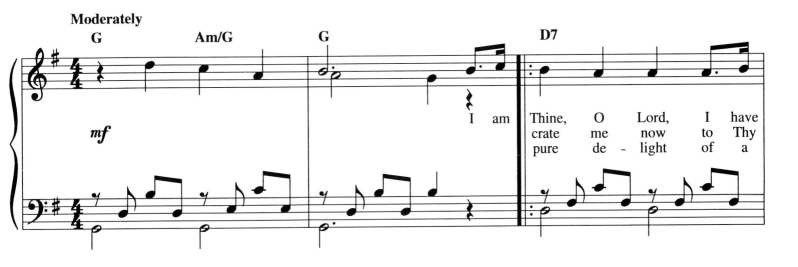

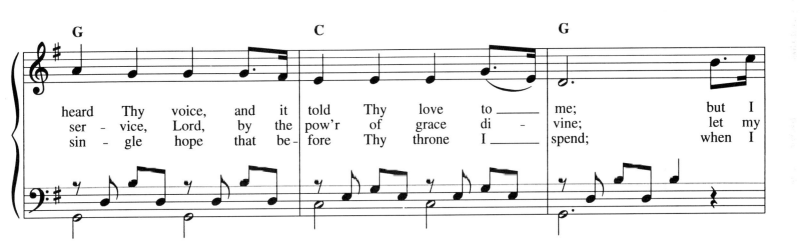

Thee.
Thine.
friend!

Draw me near - er, near - er, bless - ed Lord, to the

cross where Thou hast died; Draw me near - er, near - er,

near _ er bless - ed Lord, to Thy pre - cious, bleed - ing side.

Con - se
O, the

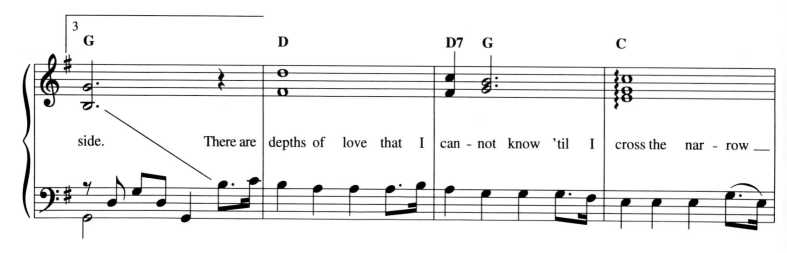

side. There are depths of love that I can - not know 'til I cross the nar - row __

"BLESSED BE THE KING THAT COMETH IN THE NAME OF THE LORD"

From the Hallmark Historical Collection. Reproduced from an original 19th century card published by Thomas De La Rue, c. 1890s.

 LOVE TO TELL THE STORY

Katherine Hankey was a Sunday school teacher who organized a class for young ladies who clerked in the shops of London. In 1866 she wrote the story of Jesus in poetic verse and entitled it "The Old, Old Story." A music teacher at Girard College, William G. Fischer, who founded a successful music store in Philadelphia, composed the music for Hankey's hymn. An effective choral conductor, he led the combined Welsh singing societies for the 1882 bicentennial celebration of the landing of William Penn, the founder of Pennsylvania.

I LOVE TO TELL THE STORY

HANKEY
William G. Fischer, 1869

Katherine Hankey, 1866

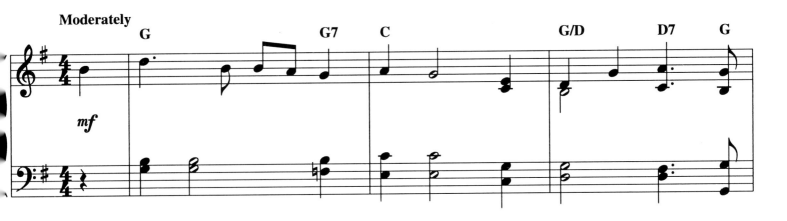

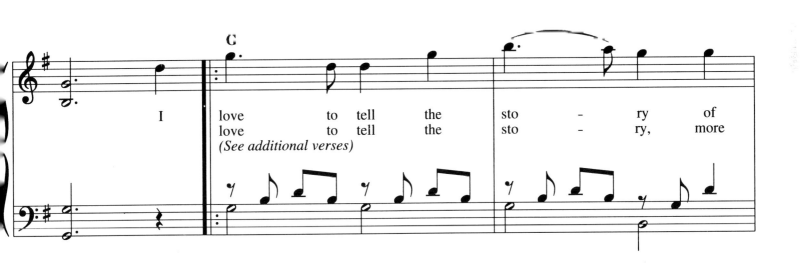

I love to tell the sto - ry of
love to tell the sto - ry, more
(See additional verses)

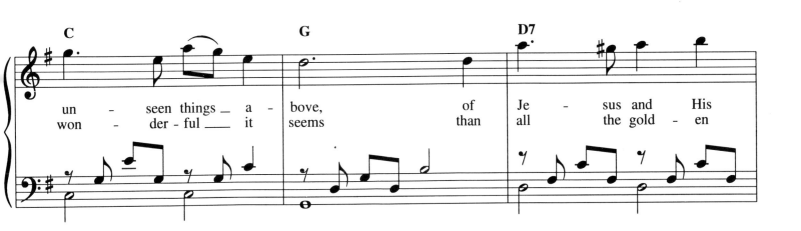

un - seen things — a - bove,   of Je - sus and His
won - der - ful __ it seems than all   the gold - en

glo - ry, of ___ Je - sus and ___ His love; I
fan - cies of ___ all our gold - en dreams;

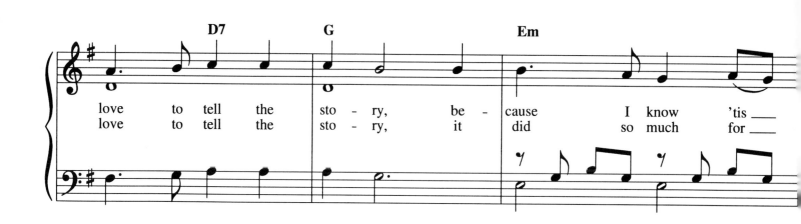

love to tell the sto - ry, be - cause I know 'tis ___
love to tell the sto - ry, it did so much for ___

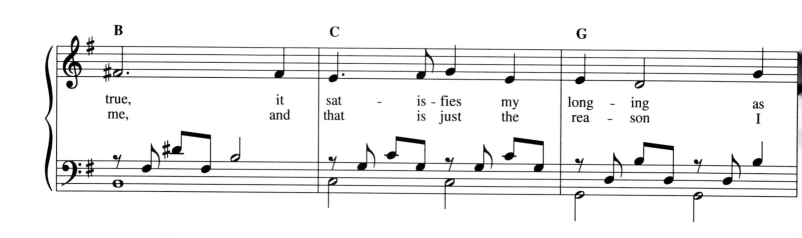

true, it sat - is - fies my long - ing as
me, and that is just the rea - son I

noth - ing else can do. I love to tell the sto - ry; 'twill
tell it now to thee.

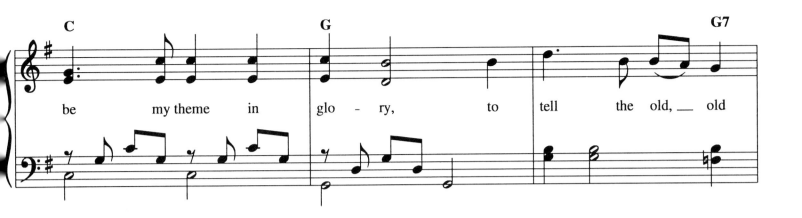

be my theme in glo - ry, to tell the old, __ old

sto - ry of Je - sus and His love. I love. To

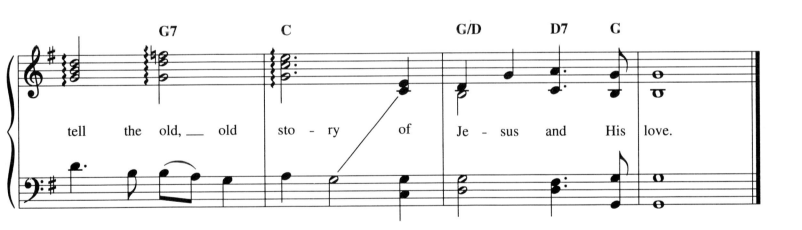

tell the old, __ old sto - ry of Je - sus and His love.

Additional Verses

3. I love to tell the story, 'tis pleasant to repeat
   What seems, each time I tell it, more wonderfully sweet;
   I love to tell the story, for some have never heard
   The message of salvation from God's own holy word.

4. I love to tell the story, for those who know it best
   Seem hungering and thirsting to hear it like the rest;
   And when in scenes of glory, I sing the new, new song,
   'Twill be the old, old story that I have loved so long.

I NEED THEE EVERY HOUR

A Brooklyn homemaker, Annie Hawks, wrote the hymn in 1872.
She related that one day she felt "a sense of nearness to the Master,
and these words, 'I need thee every hour,' were ushered into my
mind." She shared the poem with Robert Lowry, pastor of the
Hanson Place Baptist Church, Brooklyn, who composed the tune.

I NEED THEE EVERY HOUR

NEED
Robert Lowry, 1873

Annie S. Hawks, 1872

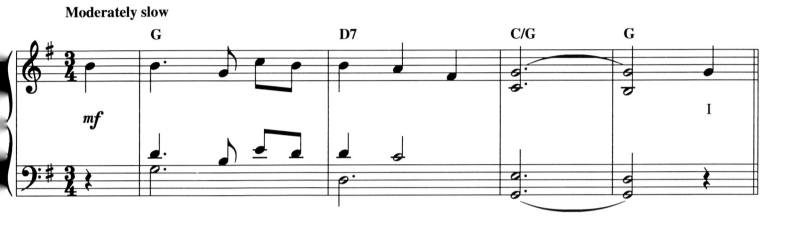

need Thee ev – 'ry hour, most gra – cious ___ Lord; no
need Thee ev – 'ry hour, most stay Thou ___ near ___ by; temp –

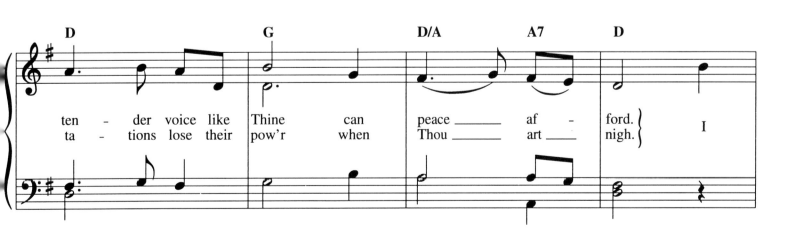

ten – der voice like Thine can peace ___ af – ford.
ta – tions lose their pow'r when Thou ___ art ___ nigh.

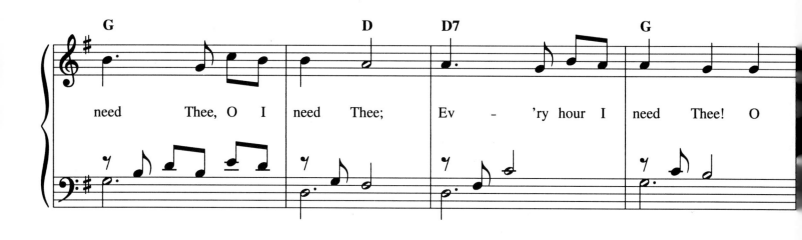

need Thee, O I need Thee; Ev - 'ry hour I need Thee! O

bless me now, my Sav - ior, I come _____ to Thee. I

Thee.

I
need Thee ev - 'ry
need Thee ev - 'ry
(See additional verse)

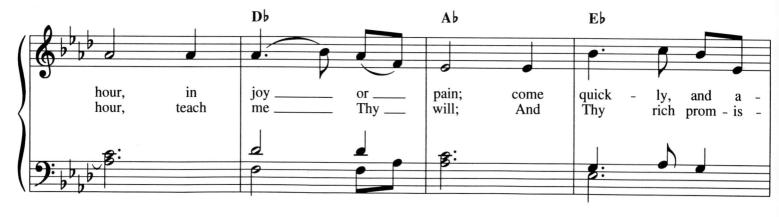

hour, in joy _____ or _____ pain; come quick - ly, and a -
hour, in teach me _____ Thy _____ will; And Thy rich prom - is -

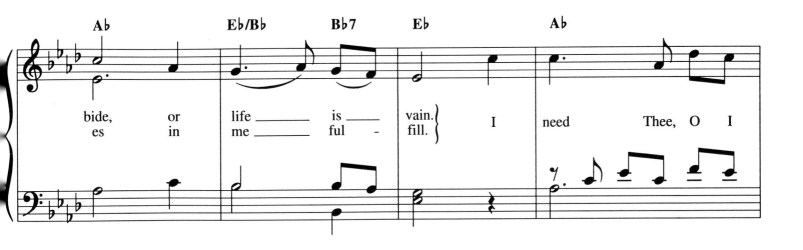

bide, or   life _____ is _____ vain.
es   in   me _____ ful - fill.

I   need   Thee, O   I

need Thee;   Ev - 'ry hour I   need   Thee! O   bless   me now, my

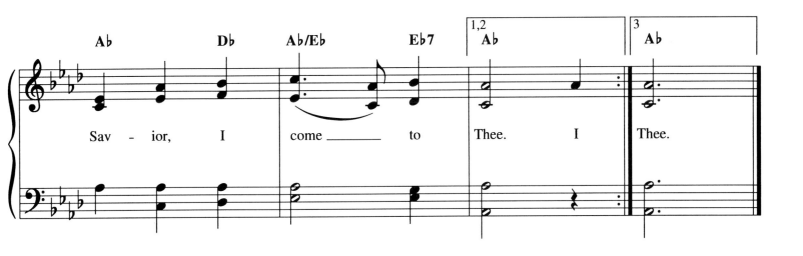

Sav - ior,   I   come _____ to   Thee.   I   Thee.

Additional Verse

5. I need Thee ev'ry hour, most Holy One;
O make me Thine indeed, Thou Blessed Son!

IN THE GARDEN

A music editor for a Philadelphia publisher, C. Austin Miles enjoyed photography as a hobby. At home he had a combination music room and photography laboratory. Sitting at his desk at home one day he read the twentieth chapter of John's Gospel. He closed his eyes and the scene described in the Scripture became as vivid to him as though he were there. Later, as he recalled this experience, he wrote both the music and the words that begin "I come to the garden alone."

IN THE GARDEN

C. Austin Miles, 1912

Tenderly

mp

I come to the gar-den a-
speaks, and the sound of His

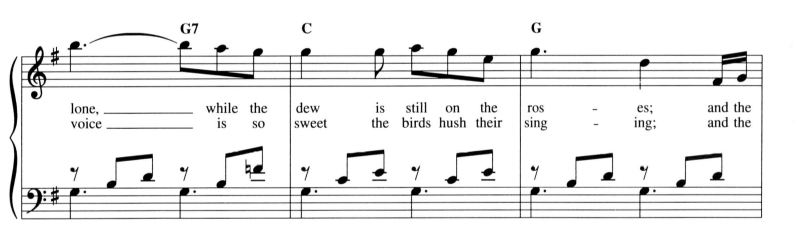

lone, _____ while the dew is still on the ros - es; and the
voice _____ is so sweet the birds hush their sing - ing; and the

voice I hear, fall-ing on my ear, the Son of God dis-
mel - o - dy that He gave to me with - in my heart is

closâ€‘es.
ringâ€‘ing. } And He walks with me, and He talks with me, and He

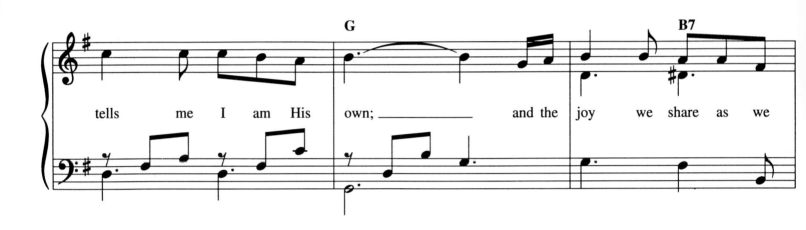

tells me I am His own; _____ and the joy we share as we

tarâ€‘ry there none othâ€‘er has evâ€‘er_____ known. _____ He known. _____ I'd

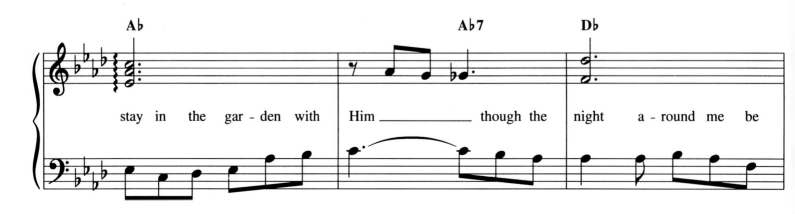

stay in the garâ€‘den with Him _____ though the night aâ€‘round me be

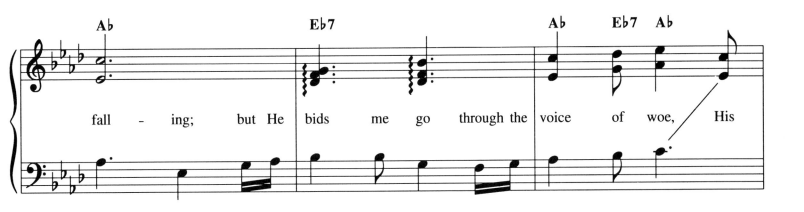

fall - ing; but He bids me go through the voice of woe, His

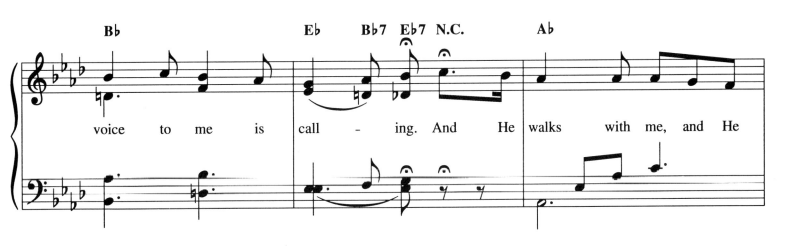

voice to me is call - ing. And He walks with me, and He

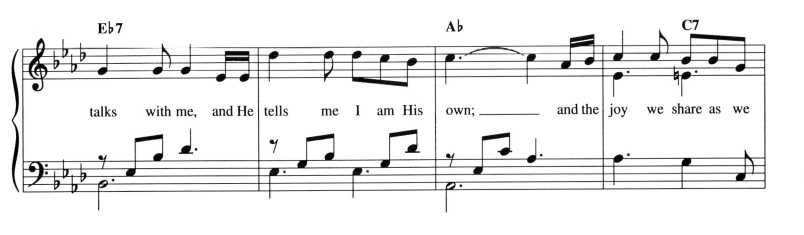

talks with me, and He tells me I am His own; _____ and the joy we share as we

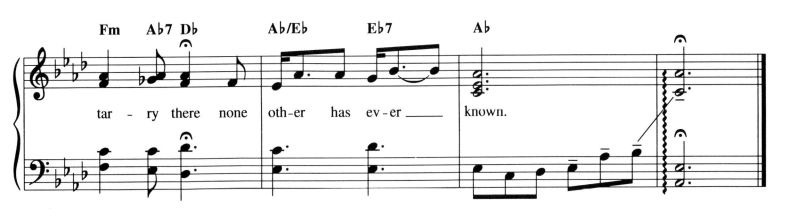

tar - ry there none oth-er has ev-er _____ known.

From the Hallmark Historical Collection. From an original 19th century greeting card published by Louis Prang of Boston, c. 1880s.

IN THE SWEET BY AND BY

Sanford Bennett operated a drug store that was a popular meeting place for folks in Elkhorn, Wisconsin. Joseph Webster, a local music teacher, frequently came by. One day he seemed depressed, and Bennett inquired as to the cause of his depression. Webster replied, "It's really nothing. It will be all right by and by." The words triggered a response in Bennett's mind, and going to his desk in the drug store, he wrote off the stanzas quickly. Webster then took his violin in hand and composed the melody for the hastily written words. The song was published in Chicago in 1868.

IN THE SWEET BY AND BY

Sanford F. Bennett, 1868

SWEET BY AND BY
Joseph P. Webster, 1868

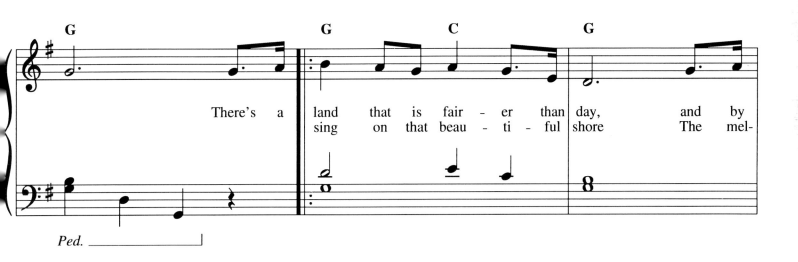

There's a land that is fair - er than day, and by
sing on that beau - ti - ful shore The mel-

Ped. _____

faith we can see it a - far; For the Fa - ther waits o - ver the
o - di - ous songs of the blest; And our spir - its shall sor - row no

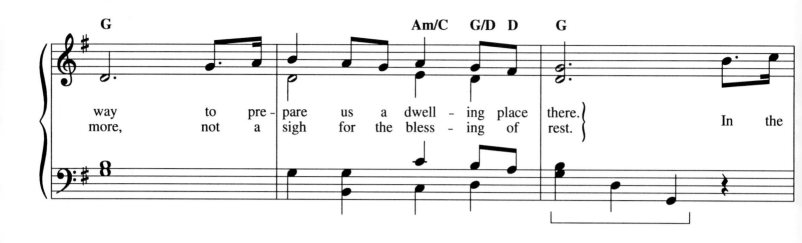

way   to   pre - pare   us   a   dwell – ing   place   there.   In   the
more,   not   a   sigh   for   the   bless – ing   of   rest.

sweet   by   and   by,   we   shall   meet   on   that   beau – ti – ful   shore;   In   the

sweet   by   and   by,   we   shall   meet   on   that   beau – ti – ful   shore.   We   shall
                                                                                                          To   our

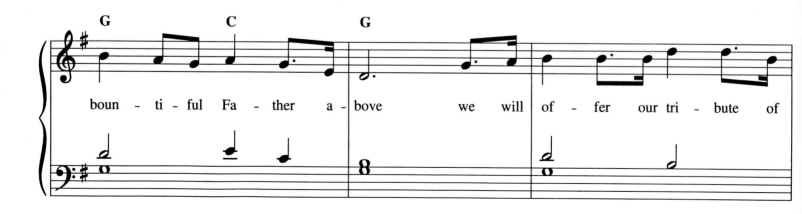

boun – ti – ful   Fa – ther   a – bove   we   will   of – fer   our   tri – bute   of

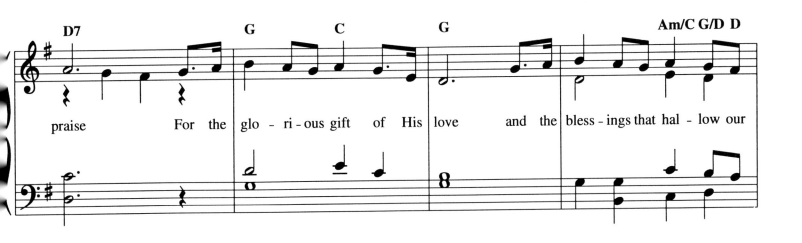

praise   For the glo - ri - ous gift of His love   and the bless - ings that hal - low our

days.   In the sweet   by and by,   we shall

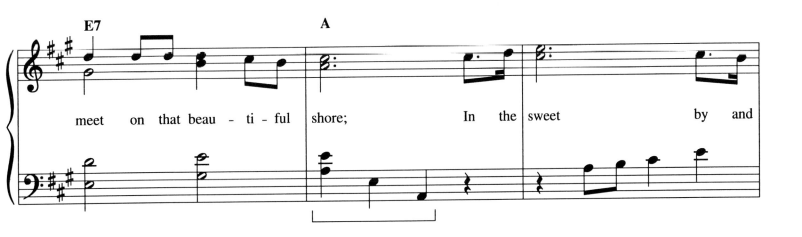

meet   on that beau - ti - ful shore;   In the sweet   by and

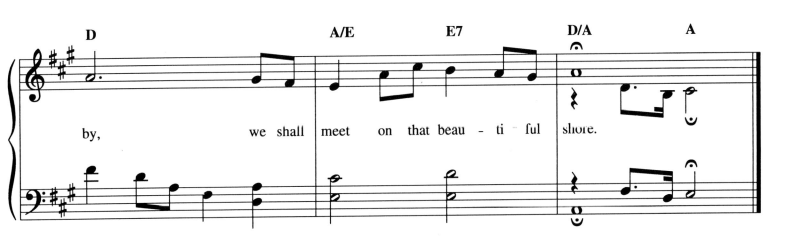

by,   we shall meet   on that beau - ti - ful shore.

*F*or God so loved
the world,
that he gave
his only begotten Son,
that whosoever
believeth in him
should not perish,
but have everlasting life.

JOHN 3:16

JESUS IS TENDERLY CALLING YOU HOME

The prolific hymn writer Fanny J. Crosby wrote the words for the hymn in the flat where she lived in Manhattan. George C. Stebbins, who composed the music, commented that he wrote the music "with the view of making the song available as an invitation hymn; but that it would meet with instant favor, and in a few years would become generally known, did not enter my mind." It was published in 1883.

JESUS IS TENDERLY CALLING YOU HOME

CALLING TODAY

Fanny J. Crosby, 1883

George C. Stebbins, 1883

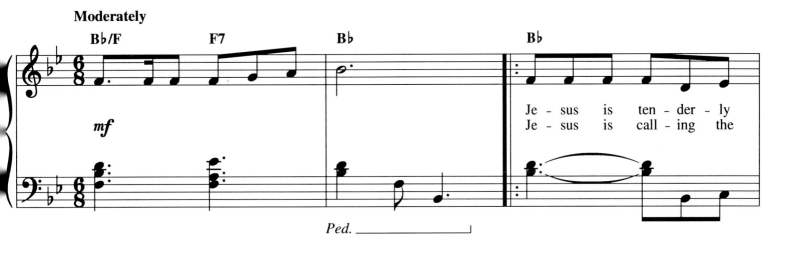

Moderately

Je - sus is ten - der - ly
Je - sus is call - ing the

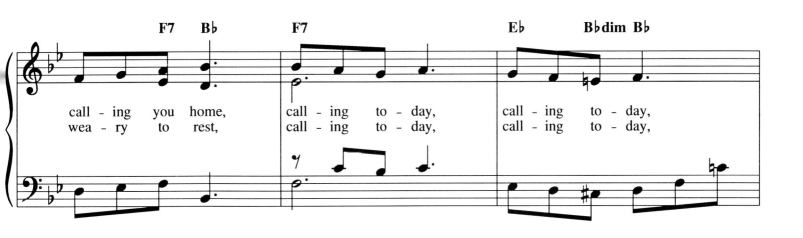

call - ing you home,   call - ing to - day,   call - ing to - day,
wea - ry to rest,   call - ing to - day,   call - ing to - day,

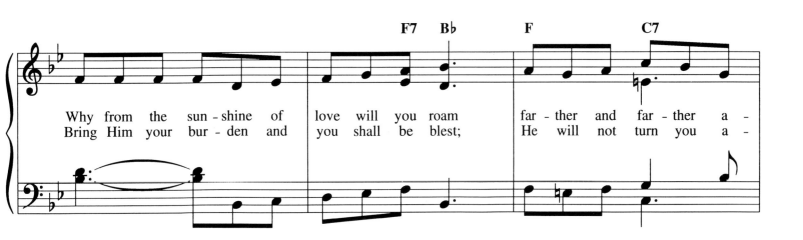

Why from the sun - shine of   love will you roam   far - ther and far - ther a -
Bring Him your bur - den and   you shall be blest;   He will not turn you a -

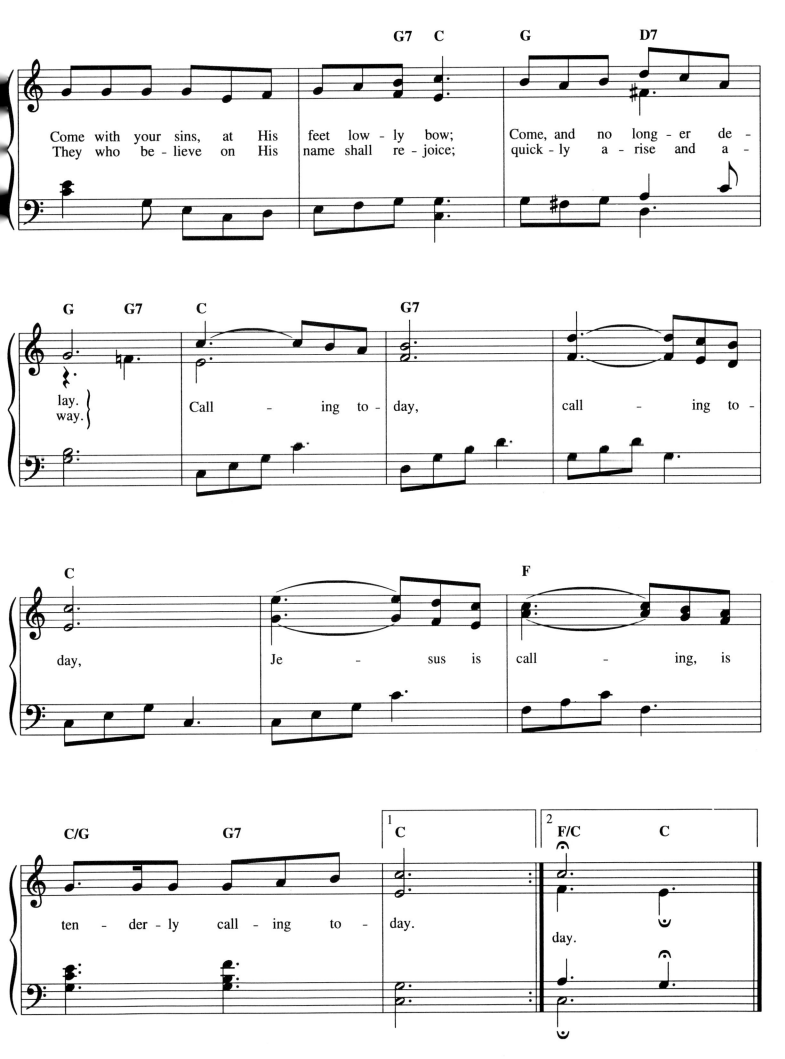

From the Hallmark Historical Collection. From an original 19th century greeting card published by Louis Prang of Boston.

JUST AS I AM

Charlotte Elliott, an invalid for most of her life, lived in Brighton, England. One day in 1834 she declined to accompany her family to an event to raise money for St. Mary's Hall, saying she did not feel well. Feeling a sense of helplessness in the midst of a sleepless night, she expressed her strong Christian faith in a poem of six stanzas. Of the many tunes written for this text, WOODWORTH, written in 1849 by William B. Bradbury, has outshone them all. In the Billy Graham Crusades, the hymn is always sung at the time of invitation.

JUST AS I AM

WOODWORTH
William B. Bradbury, 1849

Charlotte Elliott, 1834

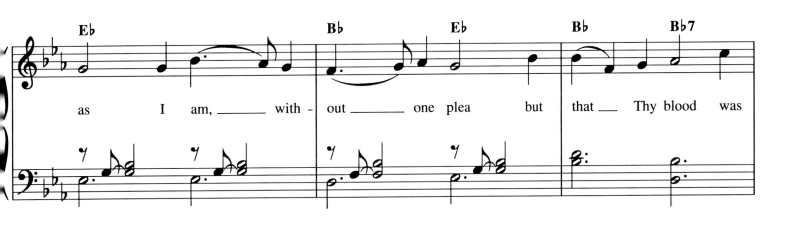

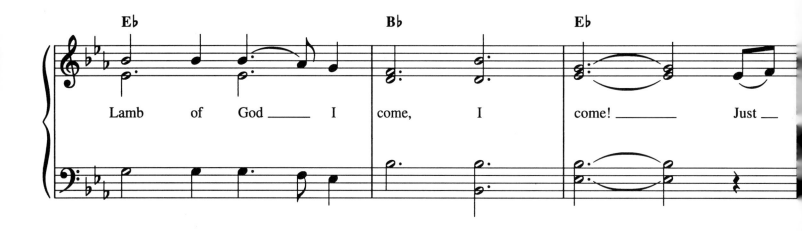

Lamb of God ____ I come, I come! _____ Just ____

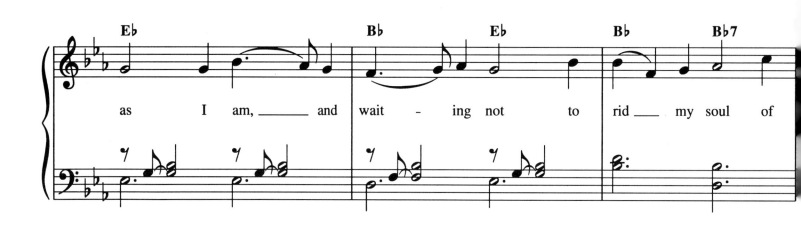

as I am, _____ and wait - ing not to rid ____ my soul of

one dark blot, to ____ Thee, whose blood _____ can cleanse each spot, _____ O

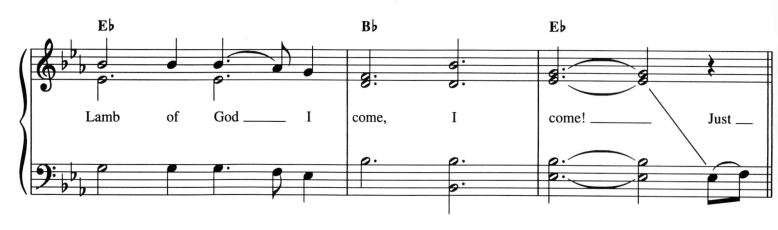

Lamb of God _____ I come, I come! _____ Just ____

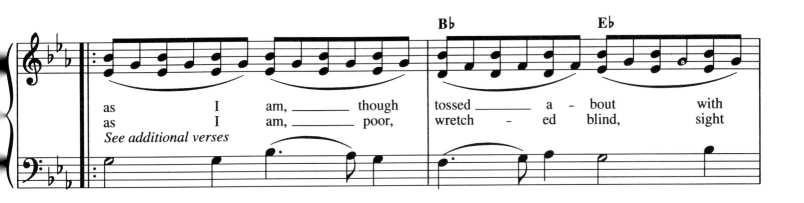

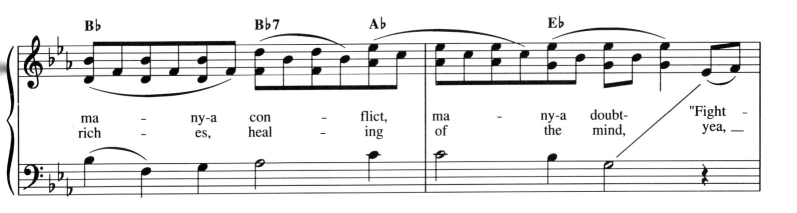

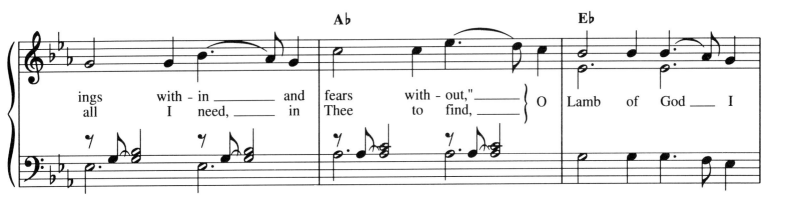

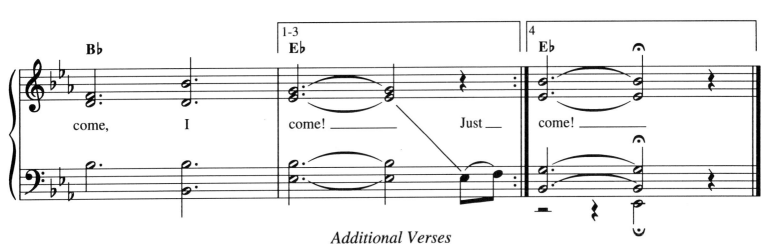

Additional Verses

5. Just as I am, Thou wilt receive, wilt welcome, pardon, cleanse, relieve;
Because Thy promise I believe, O Lamb of God, I come, I come!

6. Just as I am, Thy love I own has broken ev'ry barrier down;
Now to be Thine, and Thine alone, O Lamb of God, I come, I come!

And as they were eating, Jesus
took bread, and blessed it,
and brake it, and gave it
to the disciples, and said,
Take, eat; this is my body.

And he took the cup, and gave
thanks, and gave it to them,
saying, Drink ye all of it;
For this is my blood of the new
testament, which is shed
for many for the remission
of sins.

MATTHEW 26:26-28

LET US BREAK BREAD TOGETHER

Emerging out of spiritual tradition sometime in the nineteenth
century, the hymn is found in today's hymnals among the hymns
for Communion or the Lord's Supper. It seems to have been sung
as a "gathering song," and began "Let us praise God together
on our knees." Prior to the Emancipation Proclamation, slaves
frequently came together in secret meetings. This song, as well
as other spirituals, may have involved hidden clues about such
meetings of which only the slaves were aware.

LET US BREAK BREAD TOGETHER

Negro Spiritual, 19th century

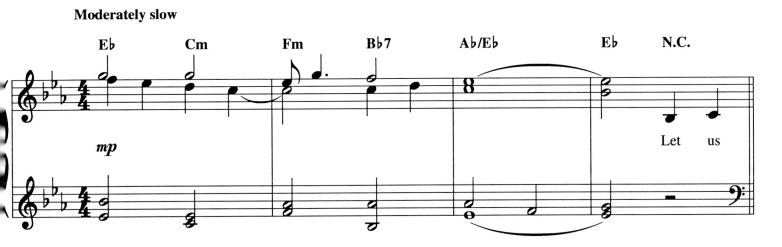

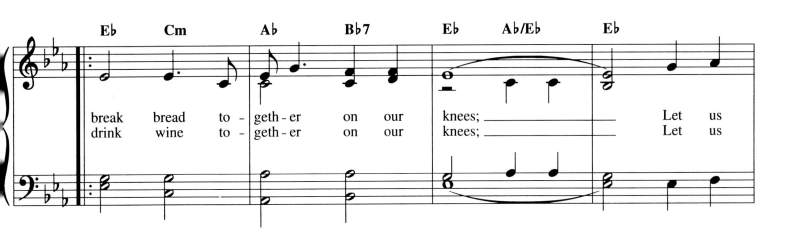

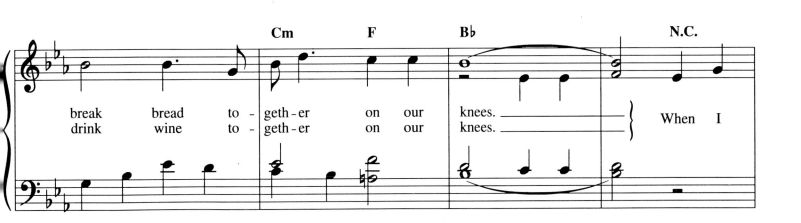

fall   on   my   knees,   with   my   face   to the ris - ing

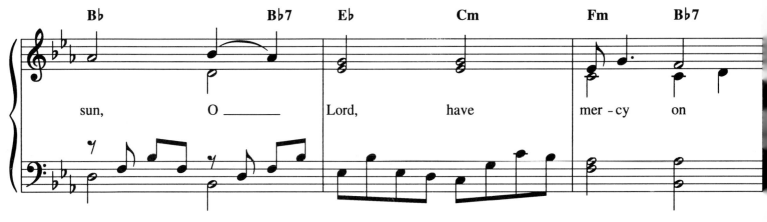

sun,   O _____ Lord,   have   mer - cy   on

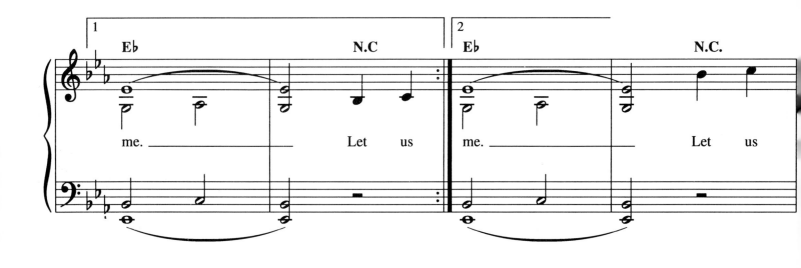

me. _____   Let   us   me. _____   Let   us

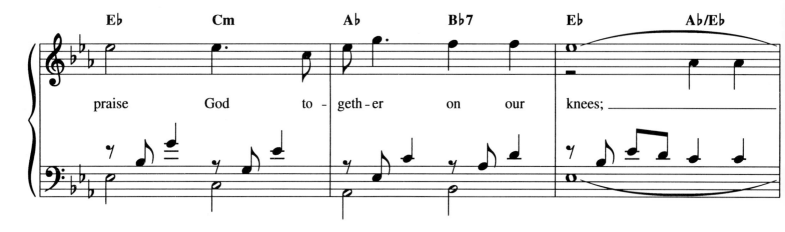

praise   God   to - geth - er   on   our   knees; _____

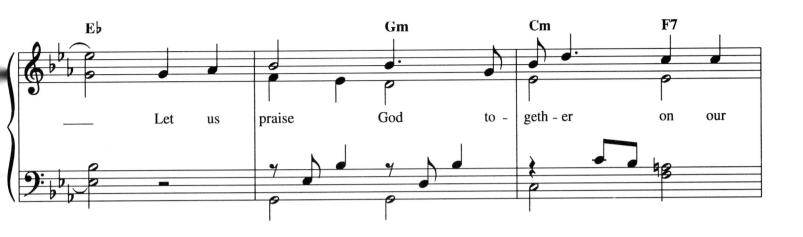

Let us praise God to- geth - er on our

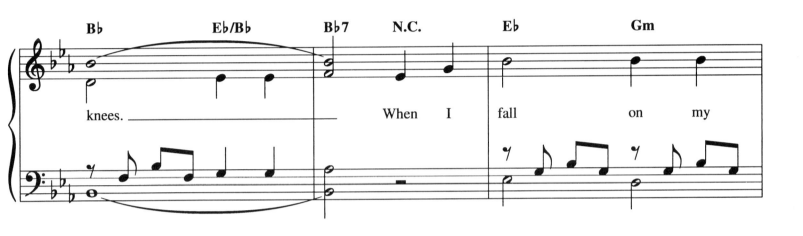

knees. When I fall on my

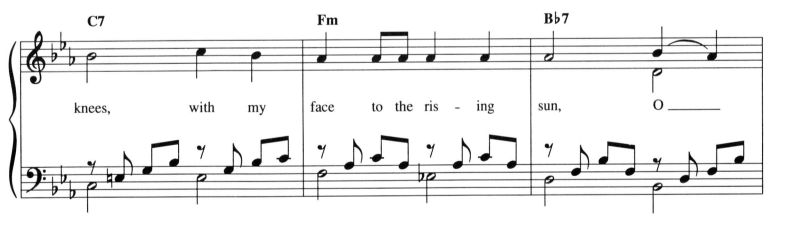

knees, with my face to the ris - ing sun, O

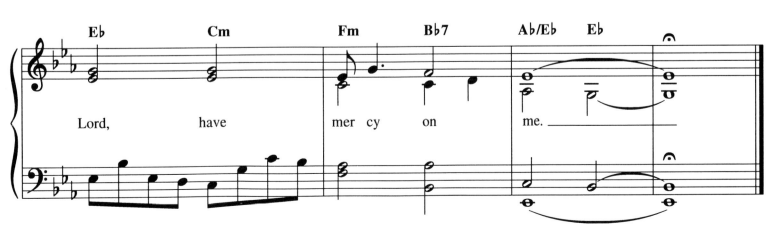

Lord, have mer cy on me.

From the Hallmark Historical Collection. *From an original 19th century greeting card published by Louis Prang of Boston.*

LOVE DIVINE, ALL LOVES EXCELLING

When Charles Wesley wrote the hymn in 1747, very few hymns made reference to the Bible teaching that God is love. The followers of John and Charles Wesley sang the hymn enthusiastically, for it reflected Wesleyan preaching. The tune for this English hymn was composed by American John Zundel in 1870. A native of Germany, Zundel served for 30 years as organist at Henry Ward Beecher's Plymouth Congregational Church in Brooklyn.

LOVE DIVINE, ALL LOVES EXCELLING

Charles Wesley, 1743

BEECHER
John Zundel, 1870

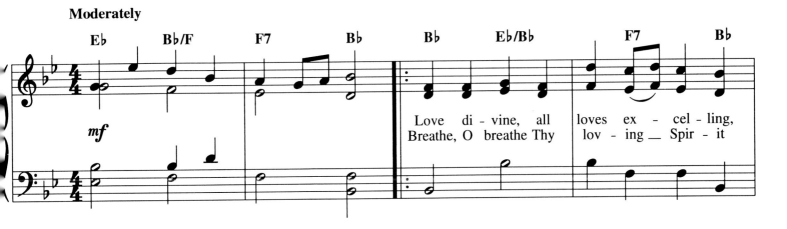

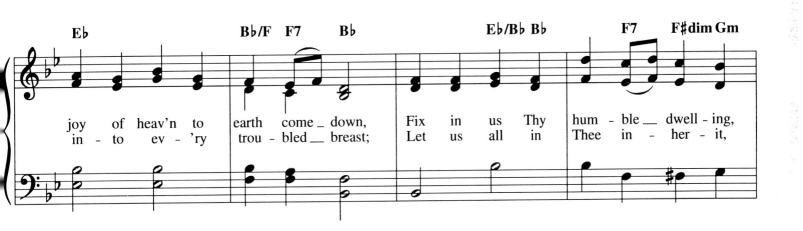

pure, un - bound - ed love Thou ___ art; Vis - it us with
Al - pha and O - me - ga ___ be; End of faith as

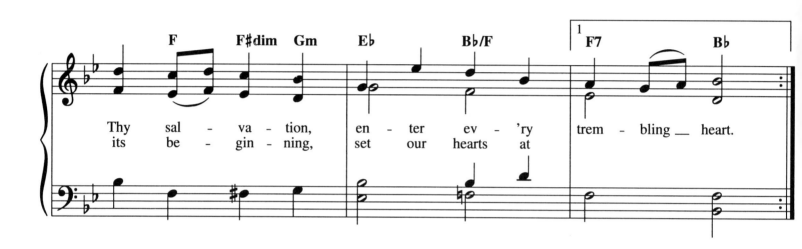

Thy sal - va - tion, en - ter ev - 'ry trem - bling ___ heart.
its be - gin - ning, set our hearts at

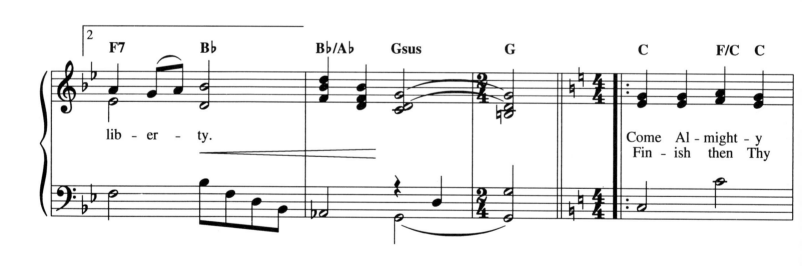

lib - er - ty. Come Al - might - y
Fin - ish then Thy

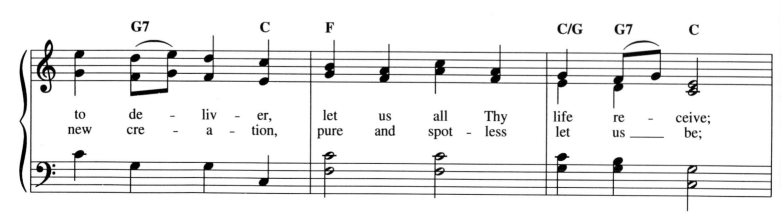

to de - liv - er, let us all Thy life re - ceive;
new cre - a - tion, pure and spot - less let us ___ be;

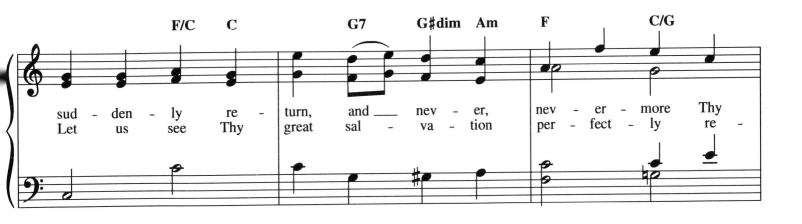

sud - den - ly re - turn, and __ nev - er, nev - er - more Thy
Let us see Thy great sal - va - tion per - fect - ly Thy re -

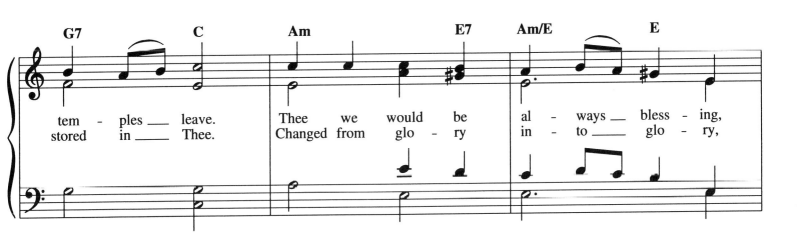

tem - ples __ leave. Thee we would be al - ways __ bless - ing,
stored in __ Thee. Changed from glo - ry in - to __ glo - ry,

serve Thee as Thy hosts a - bove, Pray, and praise Thee
'til in heav'n we take our __ place, 'til we cast our

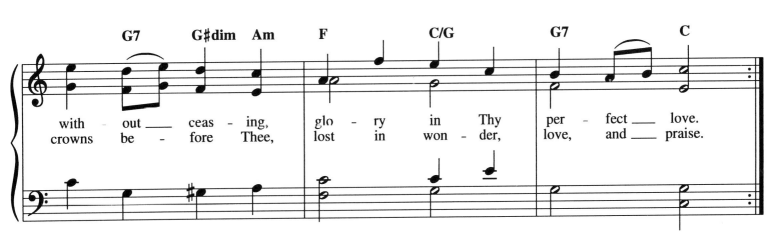

with - out __ ceas - ing, glo - ry in Thy per - fect __ love.
crowns be - fore Thee, lost in won - der, love, and __ praise.

From the Hallmark Historical Collection. *From an original 19th century card published by Louis Prang of Boston in 1885.*

 Y FAITH LOOKS UP TO THEE

Lowell Mason, a church music leader, met Ray Palmer as they were walking down a street in Boston in 1831. A recent graduate of Yale, Palmer was ordained to the Congregational ministry. Mason told him about a new hymnal he was compiling and asked if Palmer had any new hymns for his consideration. Palmer answered affirmatively and the two men stepped into a nearby store. Standing at the counter, Palmer copied off this hymn from his notebook. Later Mason composed the tune OLIVET for it and published the hymn in 1832.

MY FAITH LOOKS UP TO THEE

OLIVET
Lowell Mason, 1832

Ray Palmer, 1830

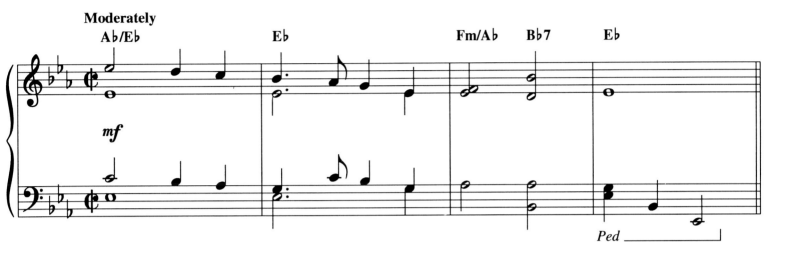

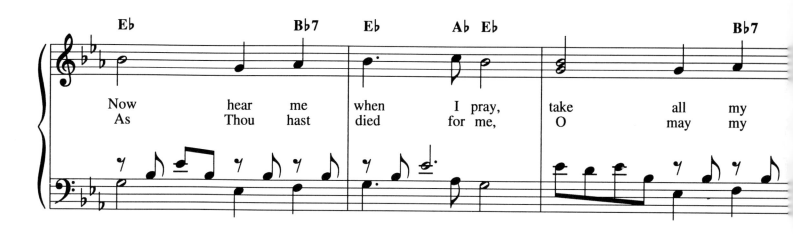

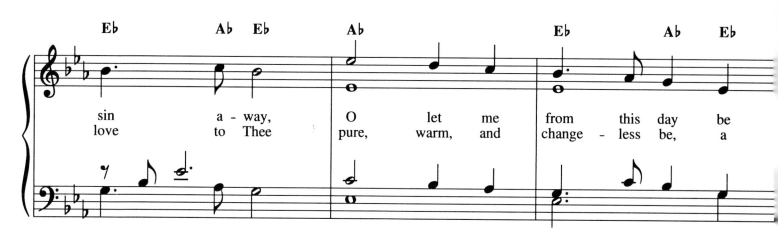

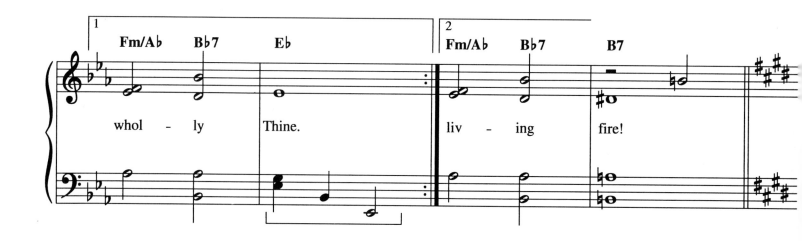

The Lord is my strength and my shield;
in him my heart trusts....

PSALM 28:7

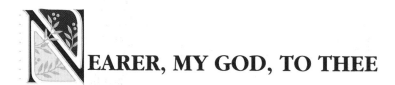EARER, MY GOD, TO THEE

Sarah Flowers Adams, a member of the Unitarian South Place
Chapel in London, wrote the hymn in 1840. She based the hymn
on the account of Jacob's dream of a ladder that reached from
earth to heaven as found in Genesis 28. Sixteen years later, Lowell
Mason, called the "father of American public school music," wrote
the tune he named BETHANY. There is a legendary story of this
hymn being sung by the passengers of the English ship *Titanic*
as it sank in the Atlantic Ocean after striking an iceberg during
its maiden voyage. More than 1,500 lives were lost.

NEARER, MY GOD, TO THEE

Sarah F. Adams, 1840

BETHANY
Lowell Mason, 1856

Near - er, my God, to Thee,
Though like the wan - der - er,

near - er to Thee!
the sun gone down,

E'en though it be a cross
Dark - ness be o - ver me,

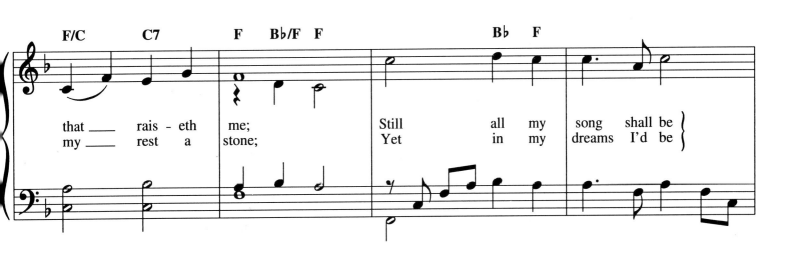

that __ rais - eth me;
my __ rest a stone;

Still all my song shall be
Yet in my dreams I'd be

147

The eyes of all wait upon Thee, O Lord; and
Thou givest them their meat in due season.

Psa. cxlv. 15.

We plough the fields, and scatter
    The good seed on the land,
But it is fed and watered
    By God's almighty hand;
He sends the snow in winter,
    The warmth to swell the grain,
The breezes and the sunshine,
    And soft refreshing rain:
        All good gifts around us
            Are sent from heaven above;
        Then thank the Lord, O thank
            the Lord,
            For all His love.

FROM THE GERMAN.

From the Hallmark Historical Collection. From an original 19th century greeting card published by Marcus Ward & Company.

NOW THANK WE ALL OUR GOD

During the Thirty Years' War, Martin Rinkart was the Lutheran minister in the walled city of Eilenburg in Saxony. War and hunger and pestilence and famine plagued the city. During 1637, Rinkart conducted 4,500 burial services, among which was that of his wife. "Now Thank We All Our God" was written in 1636 and reflects this stalwart minister's faith. There is no mention of his circumstances or difficulties. Rather he focuses on his gratitude to God, "who wondrous things hath done."

NOW THANK WE ALL OUR GOD

Martin Rinkart, 1636
tr. Catherine Winkworth, 1858

NUN DANKET
Johann Crüger, 1647

Now thank we all our God with
may this boun - teous God through

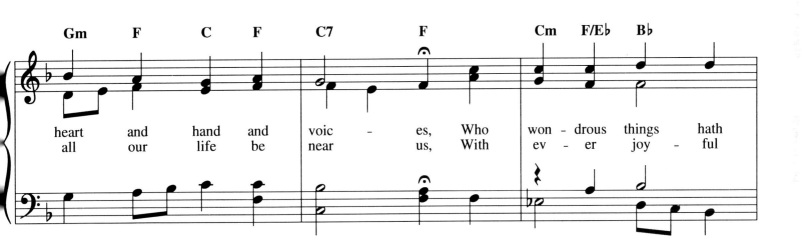

heart and hand and voic - es, Who won - drous things hath
all our life and be near us, With ev - er joy - ful

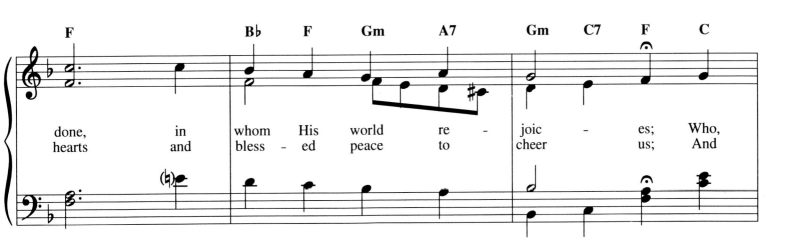

done, in whom His world re - joic - es; Who,
hearts in and bless - ed world peace to cheer us; And

from our moth - er's arms, hath blest ___ us on our
keep us in our grace, and guide ___ us when per -

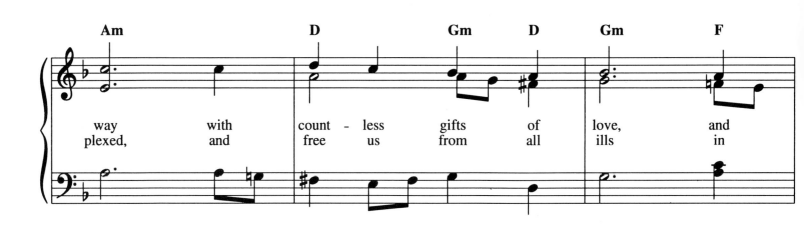

way with count - less gifts of love, and
plexed, and free us from all ills and in

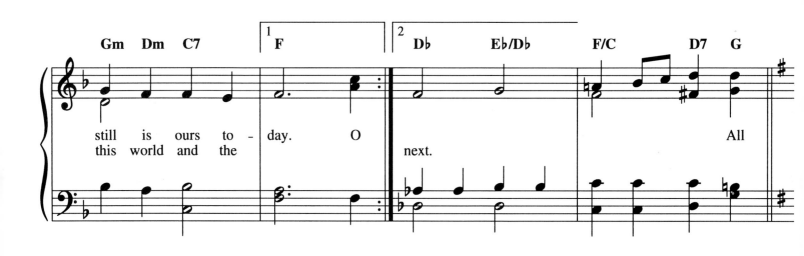

still is ours to - day. O
this world and the next.

praise All

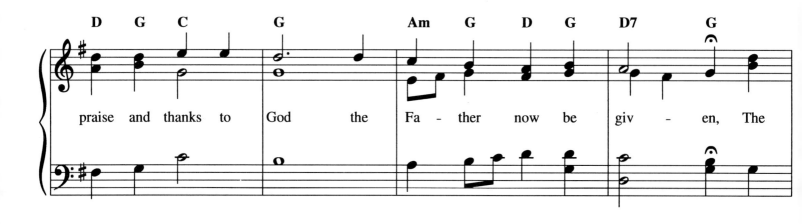

praise and thanks to God the Fa - ther now be giv - en, The

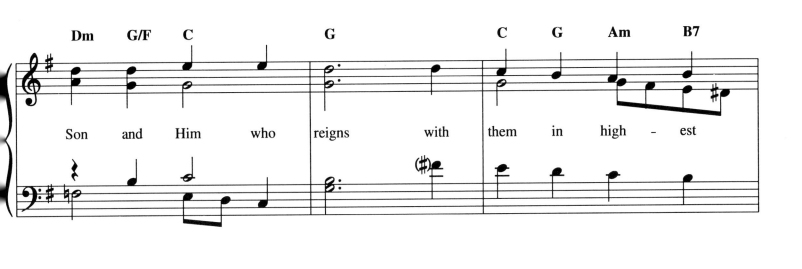

Son and Him who reigns with them in high - est

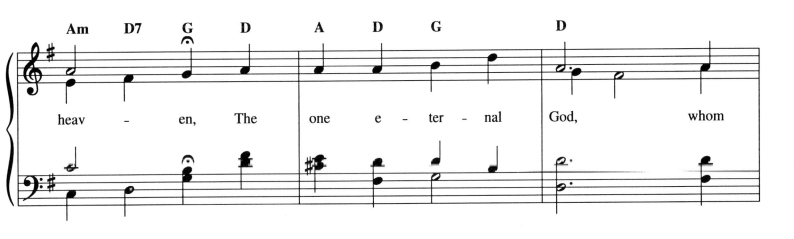

heav - en, The one e - ter - nal God, whom

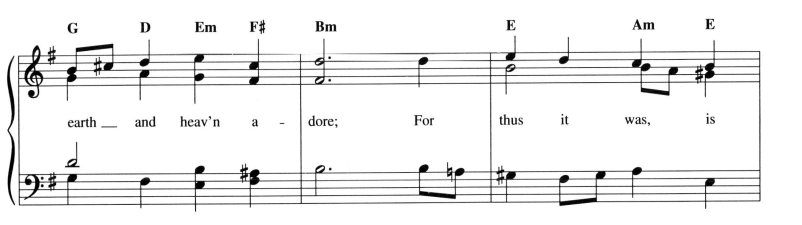

earth __ and heav'n a - dore; For thus it was, is

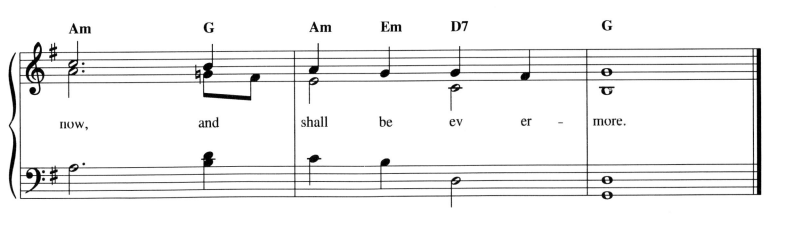

now, and shall be ev er - more.

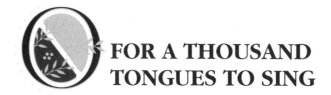

From the Hallmark Historical Collection. From an original 19th century greeting card published by G.S. Harris & Sons.

O FOR A THOUSAND TONGUES TO SING

As he approached the first anniversary of his Christian conversion, Charles Wesley recounted the abundant blessings he had received and wrote this hymn as an outpouring of his gratitude. He had heard Moravian preacher Peter Bohler say in a sermon, "If I had a thousand tongues, I would use them all to praise my God." In that moment the phrase touched Wesley's poetic genius.

O FOR A THOUSAND TONGUES TO SING

AZMON
Carl G. Glaser
arr. Lowell Mason, 1839

Charles Wesley, 1739

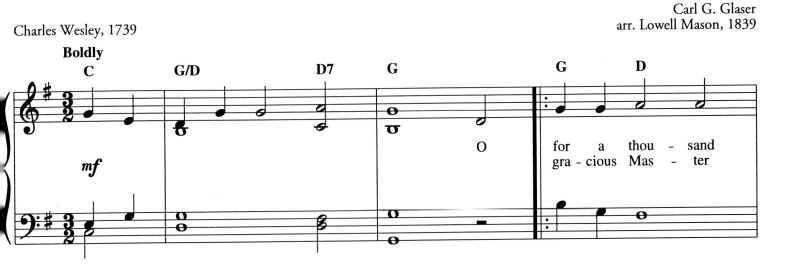

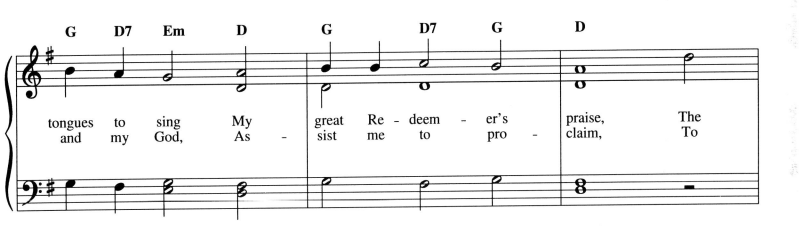

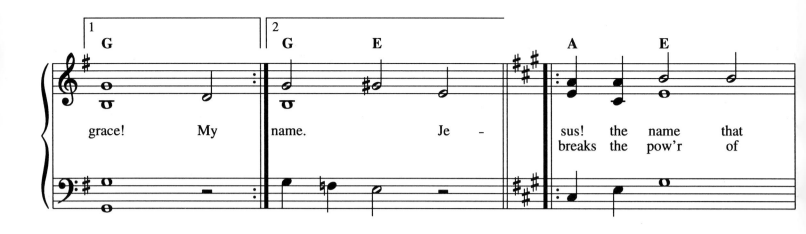

grace! My name. / Je - sus! the name that / breaks the pow'r of

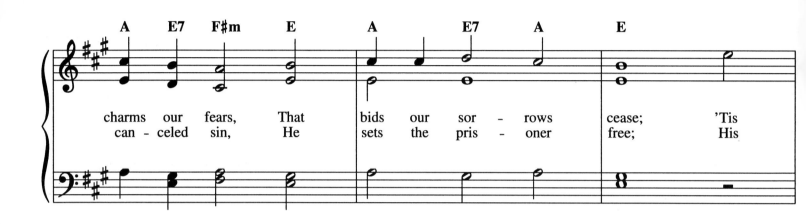

charms our fears, That / bids our sor - rows cease; 'Tis
can - celed sin, That He / sets the pris - oner free; His

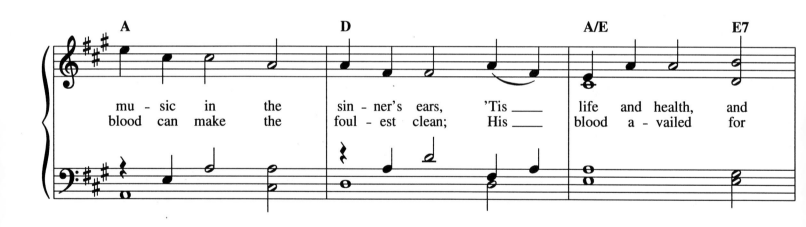

mu - sic in the / sin - ner's ears, 'Tis ___ life and health, and
blood can make the / foul - est clean; His ___ blood a - vailed for

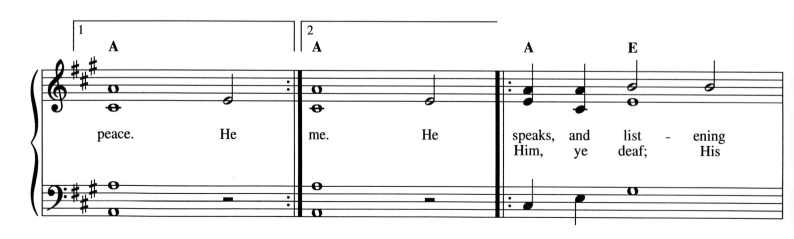

peace. He / me. He / speaks, and list - ening
Him, ye deaf; His

154

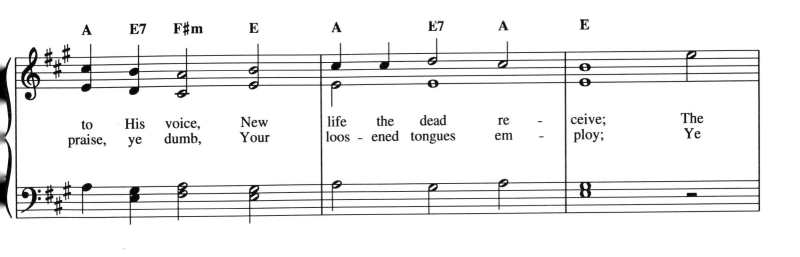

to His voice, New
praise, ye dumb, Your

life the dead re - ceive; The
loos - ened tongues em - ploy;

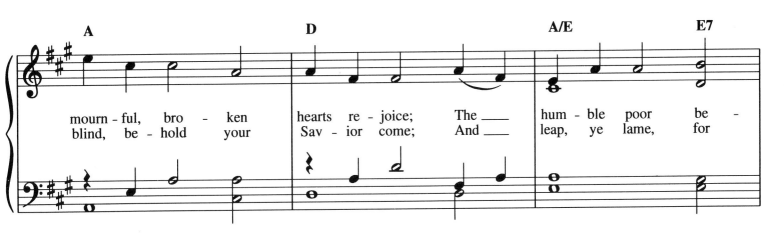

mourn - ful, bro - ken
blind, be - hold your

hearts re - joice; The ___
Sav - ior come; And ___

hum - ble poor be -
leap, ye lame, for

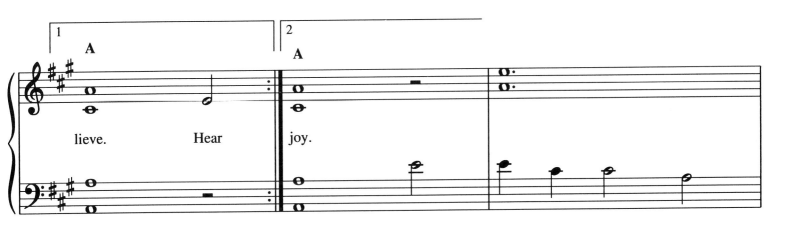

1
lieve.   Hear

2
joy.

Make a joyful noise to God, all the earth....

PSALM 66:1

ONWARD, CHRISTIAN SOLDIERS

The hymn was written by Sabine Baring-Gould in 1864 for a Children's Festival at Horbury Bridge involving a procession with cross and banners. The children sang the hymn to a melody by Joseph Haydn. Eight years later Arthur S. Sullivan (best known as half of Gilbert and Sullivan) composed a tune for the hymn, named it ST. GERTRUDE, and now it is known around the world. In recent years the hymn has come under attack for being "too martial." Ironically, such attacks reinforce one of the themes of the hymn: that the followers of Christ will meet with hostility.

ONWARD, CHRISTIAN SOLDIERS

ST. GERTRUDE
Arthur S. Sullivan, 1871

Sabine Baring-Gould, 1864

Gallantly

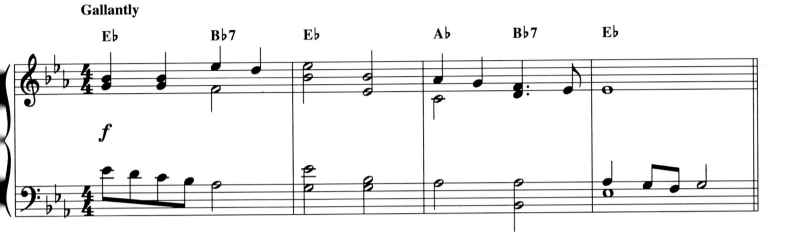

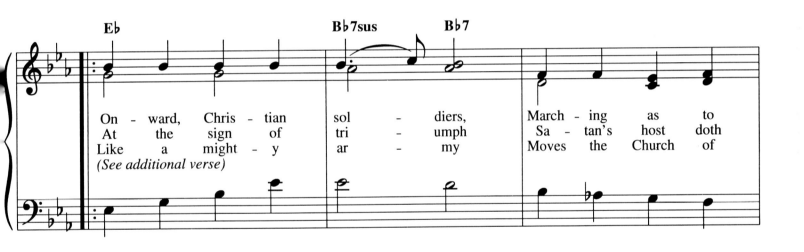

On - ward, Chris - tian sol - diers,   March - ing   as   to
At   the   sign   of   tri - umph   Sa - tan's   host   doth
Like   a   might - y   ar - my   Moves   the   Church   of

(See additional verse)

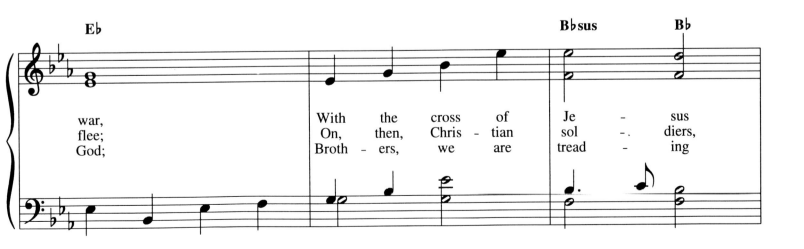

war,   With   the   cross   of   Je - sus
flee;   On,   then,   Chris - tian   sol - diers,
God;   Broth - ers,   we   are   tread - ing

F7   B♭   E♭

Go - ing on be - fore!   Christ, the roy - al Mas - ter,
On to vic - to - ry!   Hell's foun - da - tions quiv - er
Where the saints have trod!   We are not di - vid - ed,

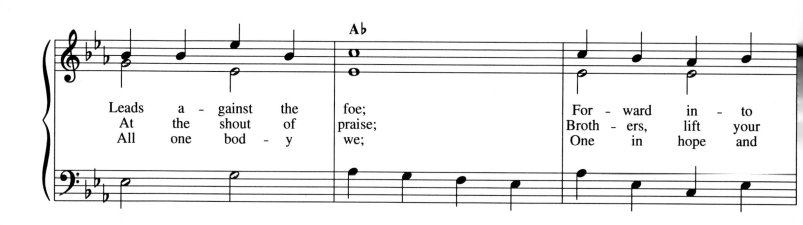

A♭

Leads a - gainst the foe;   For - ward in - to
At the shout of praise;   Broth - ers, lift your
All one bod - y we;   One in hope and

Fm/A♭   F7   B♭   1-3   E♭

bat - tle ___ See His ban - ners go!
voic - es, ___ Loud your an - thems raise!
doc - trine, ___ One in char - i - ty.

On - ward Chris - tian

B♭7   E♭   B♭7

sol - diers, ___ march - ing as to ___ war,   With the cross of

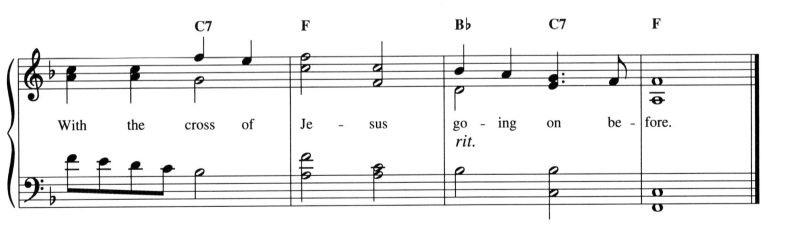

Additional Verse

Onward, then, ye people, join our happy throng;
Blend with ours your voices in the triumph song.
Glory, laud and honor unto Christ the King.
This through countless ages men and angels sing.

PEACE IN THE VALLEY

Thomas A. Dorsey wrote the song in the late 1930s amid the news of Hitler's invasions in Europe. On a train trip from Chicago to Cincinnati, Dorsey looked out the window at the cows, horses, sheep, and hogs all grazing peacefully together in a valley. He wondered people could not live together peacefully, and penciled the line "There will be peace in the valley for me someday." Back in Chicago he completed the song, and it was first recorded by Mahalia Jackson, lead singer in his church choir, not yet nationally known. But it was the recordings of Red Foley and Elvis Presley that made the song immensely popular.

(THERE'LL BE)
PEACE IN THE VALLEY
(FOR ME)

Thomas A. Dorsey, 1939

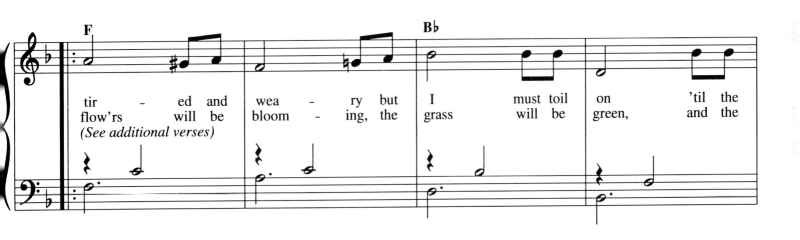

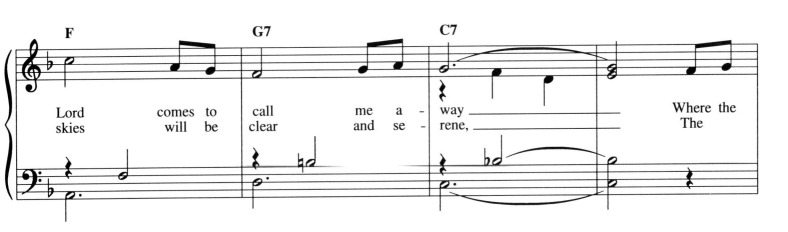

morn - ing is bright and the Lamb is the light and the
sun ev - er shines, giv - ing one is end - less beam and no

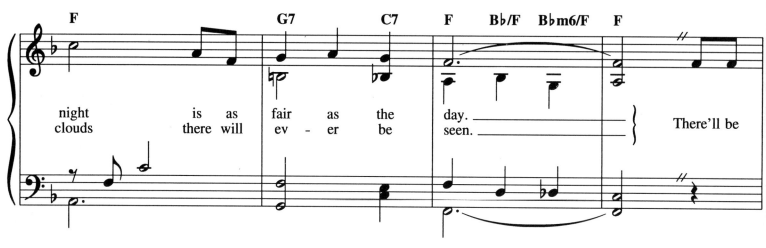

night is as fair as the day. _____ There'll be
clouds there will ev - er be seen. _____

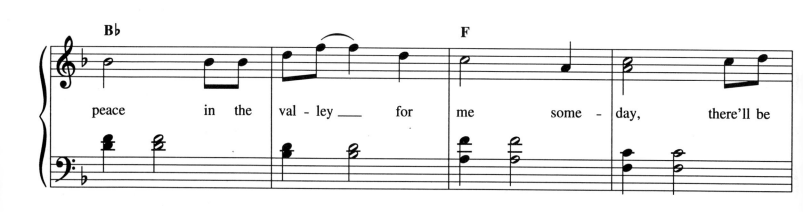

peace in the val - ley _____ for me some - day, there'll be

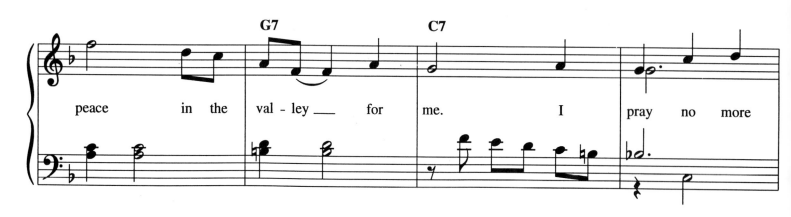

peace in the val - ley _____ for me. I pray no more

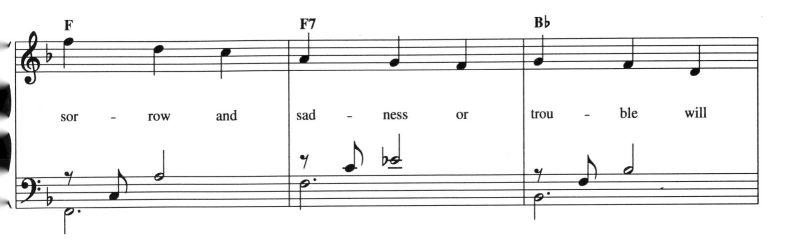

sor - row and   sad - ness or   trou - ble will

be,   there'll be   peace _____ in the   val - ley _____ for

me. _____   There the   me. _____

Additional Verses

(3.) There the bear will be gentle, the wolf will be tame,
And the lion will lay down with the lamb.
The host from the wild will be led by a Child,
I'll be changed from the creature I am.

(4.) No headaches or heartaches or misunderstands,
No confusion or trouble won't be.
No frowns to defile, just a big endless smile,
There'll be peace and contentment for me.

PRECIOUS LORD, TAKE MY HAND

Thomas A. Dorsey and his wife Nettie lived in south Chicago in 1932 and were expecting their first child. Dorsey went to St. Louis to sing in a revival meeting. In a few days he received a call that his wife was very ill and he returned to Chicago. To his sorrow, he learned that while he was en route Nettie had died in childbirth and the baby had died also. In the days that followed he found solace in his music and wrote the plaintive song "Precious Lord, Take My Hand."

PRECIOUS LORD, TAKE MY HAND

(a.k.a. TAKE MY HAND, PRECIOUS LORD)

Thomas A. Dorsey, 1932

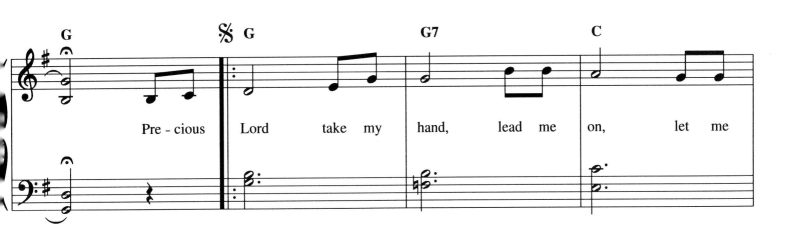

Pre - cious Lord take my hand, lead me on, let me

stand, __ I am tired, __ I am weak, I am worn. _____

Through the storm, through the night, lead me on to the

light, __ take my hand __ pre-cious Lord, _____ lead me home. _____

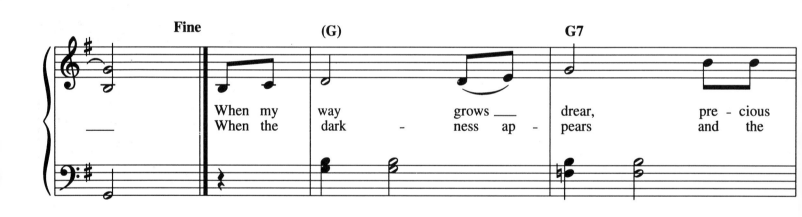

Fine

When my way grows __ drear, pre - cious
When the dark - ness ap - pears and the

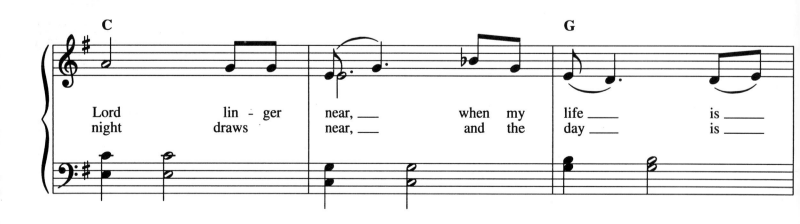

Lord lin - ger near, __ when my life ____ is ____
night draws near, __ and the day ____ is ____

167

From the Hallmark Historical Collection. *From an original 19th century greeting card published by Louis Prang of Boston, c. 1880s.*

ROCK OF AGES

Augustus Toplady, a friend of John Wesley's at one time, wrote the hymn in 1775. He points to Christ as the Rock of Ages where one may find refuge. Erik Routley has written, "All sociology, all psychology, all medicine and science come to this at last, that a man needs friendship with God, and in that will find friendship with the world. He needs a rock for shelter, a rock for refreshment, a rock for forgiveness. That Rock is Christ."

ROCK OF AGES

Augustus M. Toplady, 1775

TOPLADY
Thomas Hastings, 1832

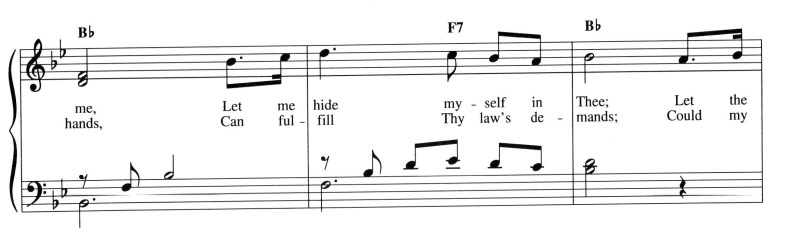

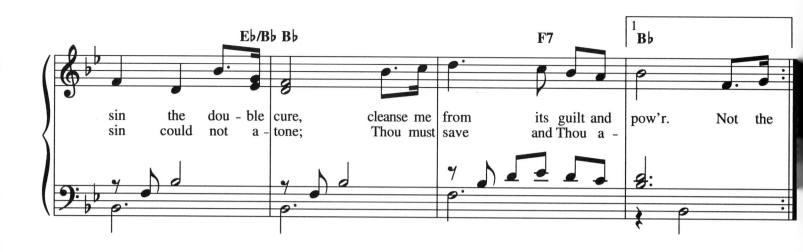

sin the dou – ble cure, cleanse me from its guilt and pow'r. Not the
sin could not a – tone; Thou must save and Thou a –

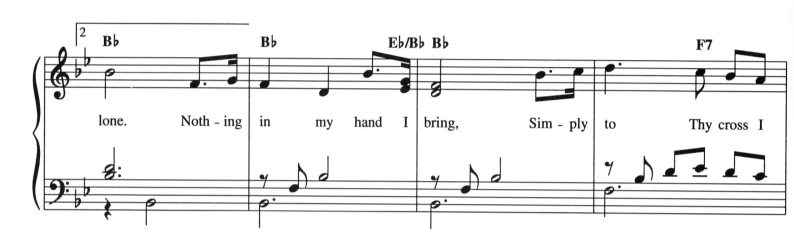

lone. Noth – ing in my hand I bring, Sim – ply to Thy cross I

cling; Na – ked, come to Thee for dress, Help – less, look to Thee for

grace, Foul, I to the foun – tain fly, wash me Sav – ior, or I

170

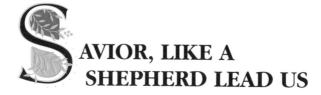

SAVIOR, LIKE A SHEPHERD LEAD US

The hymn first appeared anonymously in a collection of hymns for children issued in 1836 in England. Both Psalm 23 and the New Testament parable of the Good Shepherd are reflected in the lines of the hymn. The music was composed by William B. Bradbury, who included it in a collection of Sunday school songs published in New York City in 1859.

SAVIOR, LIKE A SHEPHERD LEAD US

Anon., 1836

BRADBURY
William B. Bradbury, 1859

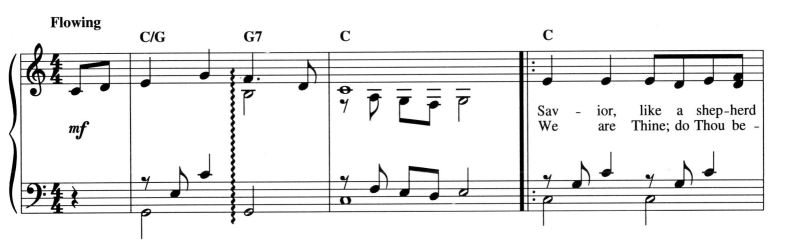

Savior, like a shep-herd
We are Thine; do Thou be -

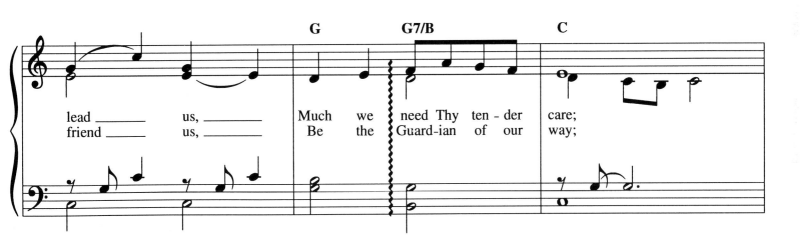

lead _____ us, _____
friend _____ us, _____
Much we need Thy ten - der care;
Be the Guard-ian of our way;

In Thy pleas-ant pas-tures feed _____ us, _____ For our use Thy folds pre -
Keep Thy flock, from sin de-fend _____ us, _____ Seek us when we go a -

From the Hallmark Historical Collection. *From an original 19th century greeting card published by Louis Prang of Boston.*

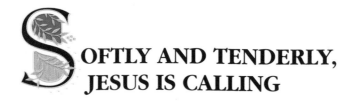 SOFTLY AND TENDERLY, JESUS IS CALLING

Will Thompson, a graduate of the New England Conservatory of Music and the music conservatory in Leipzig, wrote both words and music in 1880. D.L. Moody, the evangelist, shortly before he died, told Thompson, "I would rather have written 'Softly and Tenderly' than anything I have been able to do in my whole life." Thompson's song was sung at the memorial services for Martin Luther King, Jr., by the choir of the Ebenezer Baptist Church in Atlanta, Georgia, April 8, 1968.

SOFTLY AND TENDERLY, JESUS IS CALLING

Will L. Thompson, 1880

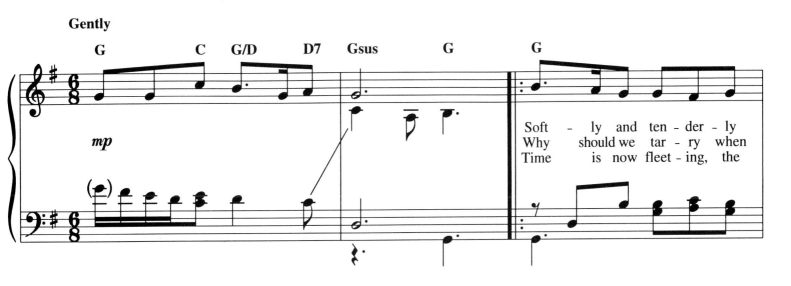

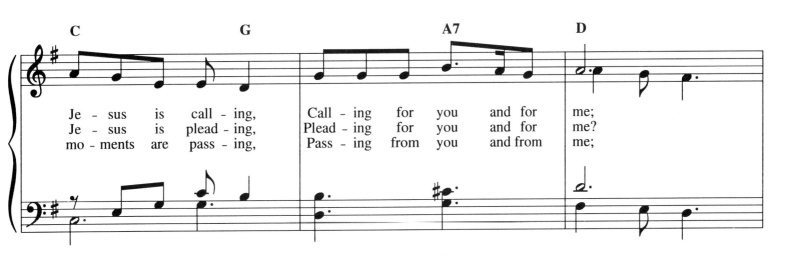

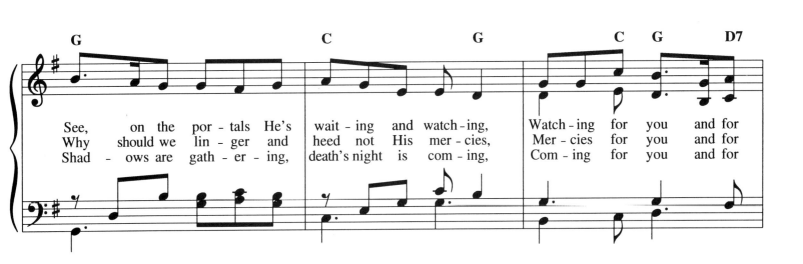

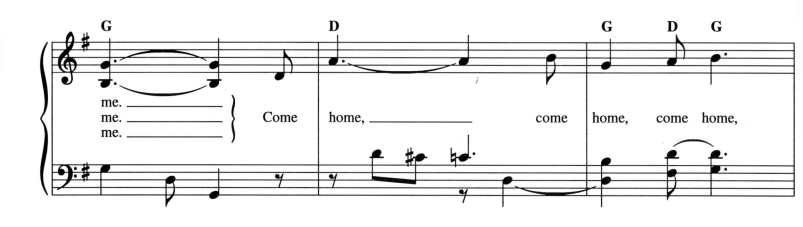

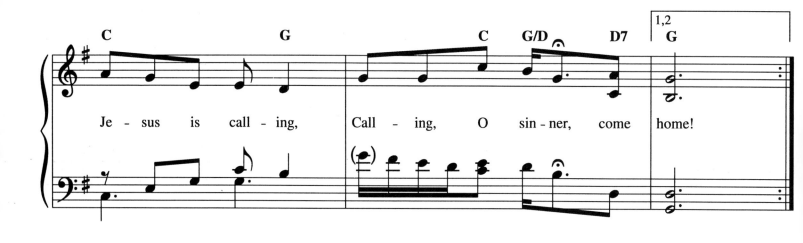

178

...By his great mercy we have been born anew to a living hope through the resurrection of Jesus Christ...

I PETER 1:3

STAND UP, STAND UP FOR JESUS

During the spiritual awakening that swept through Philadelphia in 1858, a young Episcopal minister was fatally injured in an accident. George Duffield, a Presbyterian minister and his close friend, stood by his bed as he died. His last exhortation to Duffield was "Tell them, 'Let us stand up for Jesus.'" The following Sunday morning Duffield preached to his congregation Ephesians 6:14, and concluded the sermon by reading this hymn he had written after his friend's death.

STAND UP, STAND UP FOR JESUS

George Duffield, Jr., 1858

WEBB
George J. Webb, 1830

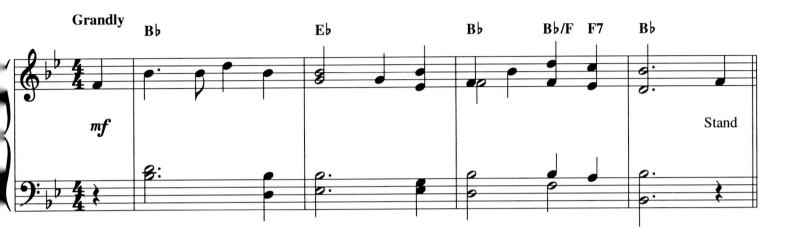

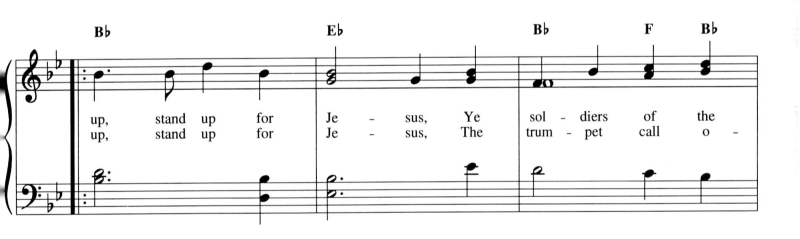

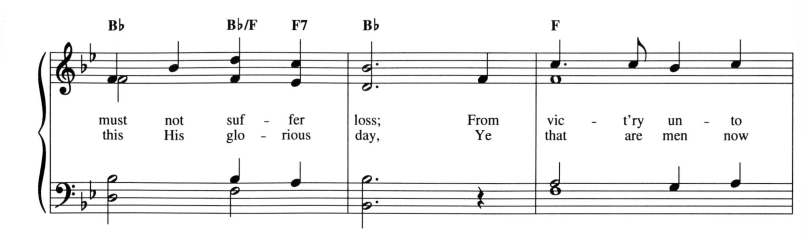

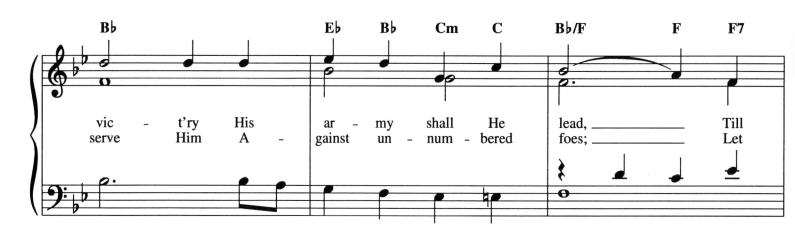

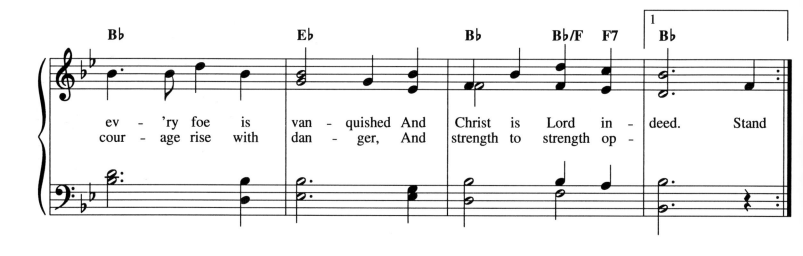

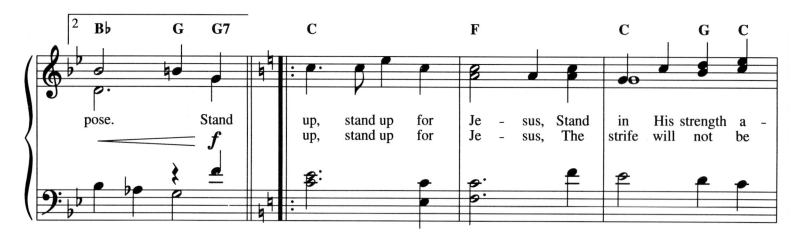

SWEET HOUR OF PRAYER

The hymn of five stanzas was printed in a New York newspaper on September 13, 1845, with the notice that it had been written by a blind preacher of Coleshill, England. Efforts to identify this person have been unsuccessful. Somehow the poem came to the attention of William B. Bradbury, who composed the music and published it in a Sunday school song book in 1860. It remains a favorite hymn throughout the world.

SWEET HOUR OF PRAYER

SWEET HOUR
William B. Bradbury, c. 1861

William Walford, c. 1840

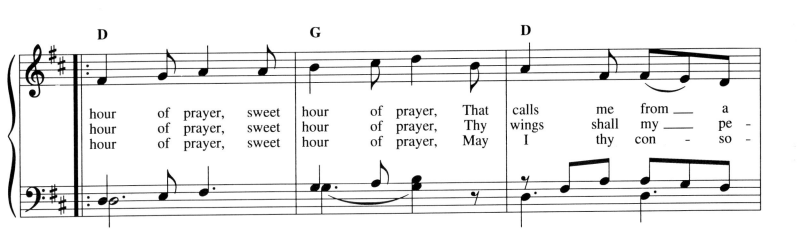

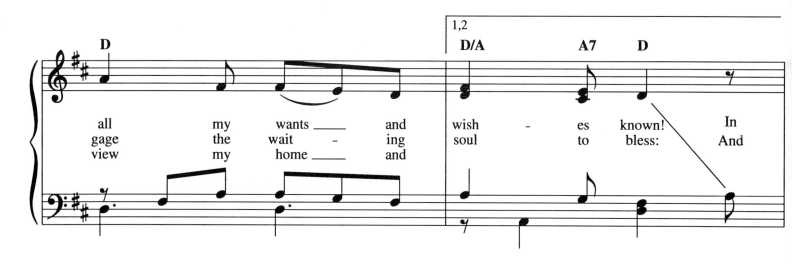

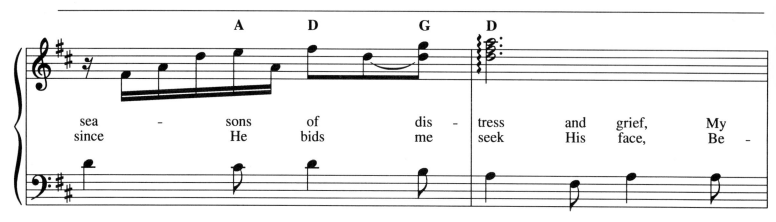

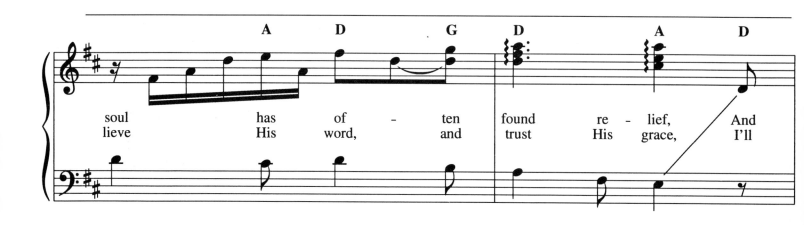

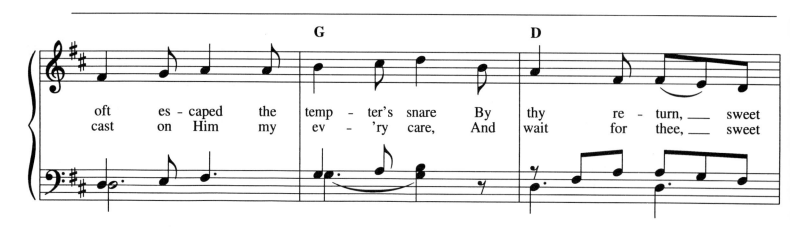

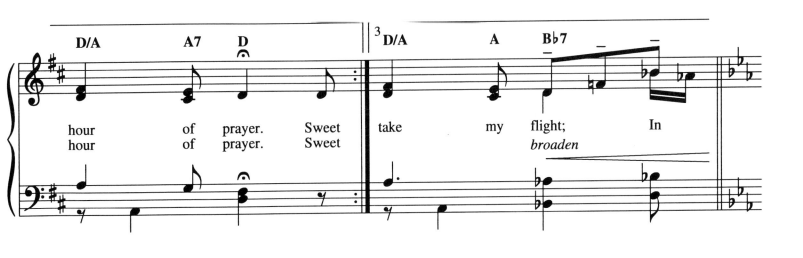

hour   of   prayer.   Sweet   take   my   flight;   In
hour   of   prayer.   Sweet   Sweet   *broaden*

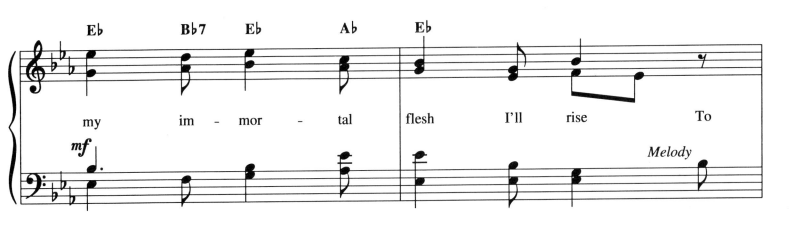

my   im -   mor -   tal   flesh   I'll   rise   To

Melody

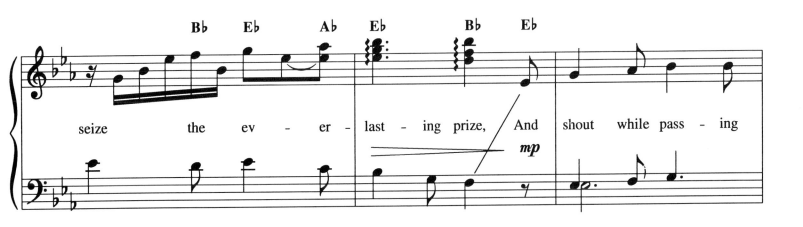

seize   the   ev - er - last - ing prize,   And   shout   while pass - ing

through   the   air,   Fare - well,   fare - well ___ sweet   hour   of   prayer!

rit.

I keep the Lord
always before me;
because he is at my right hand,
I shall not be moved.

PSALM 16:8

TAKE MY LIFE AND LET IT BE

In December 1874, Frances Havergal went with a group of friends for a five-day trip. A devout Christian, Havergal was concerned for some of the group who were not believing Christians. She prayed earnestly for them and then had the joy of leading them to accept Christ as Savior. Joy overflowed her heart and she wrote a poem of 12 couplets beginning:

> Take my life and let it be
> Consecrated, Lord, to thee.

TAKE MY LIFE AND LET IT BE

HENDON
Henri A. C. Malan, 1823
harm. Lowell Mason, 1841

Frances R. Havergal, 1874

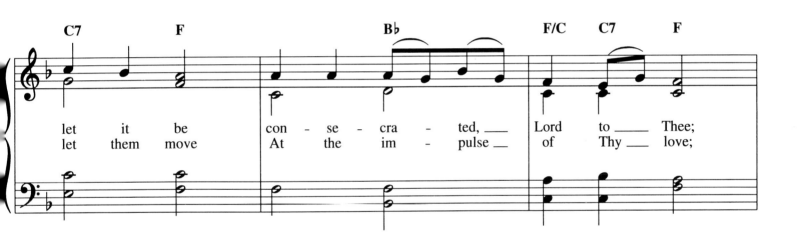

From the Hallmark Historical Collection. From an original 19th century greeting card published by Marcus Ward & Company.

THE CHURCH'S ONE FOUNDATION

In 1866 a great furor arose in the Church of England over the questioning of the historicity of the Pentateuch – the first five books of the Old Testament. Samuel J. Stone, curate at Windsor, England, a stalwart defender of the Holy Scripture, published 12 hymns based on the Apostles' Creed. The ninth article of the Creed was the basis for "The Church's One Foundation." The hymn tune AURELIA was composed by Samuel Sebastian Wesley, grandson of Charles Wesley, the hymn writer.

THE CHURCH'S ONE FOUNDATION

AURELIA
Samuel S. Wesley, 1864

Samuel J. Stone, 1866

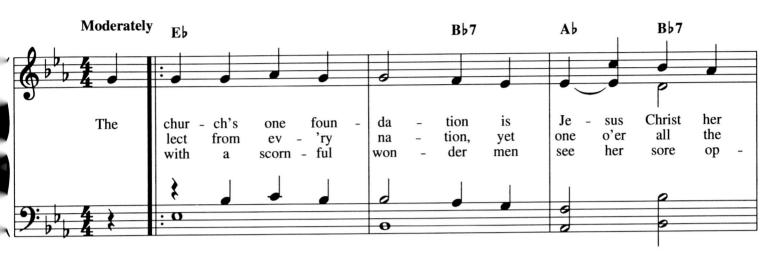

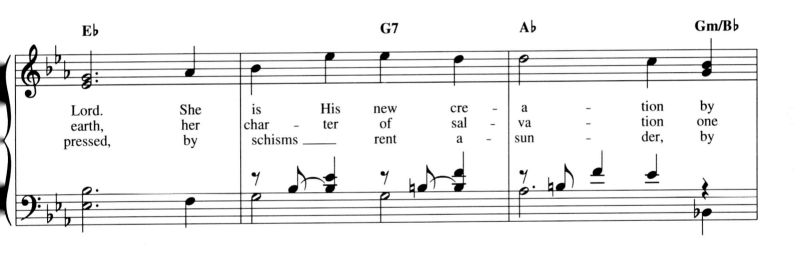

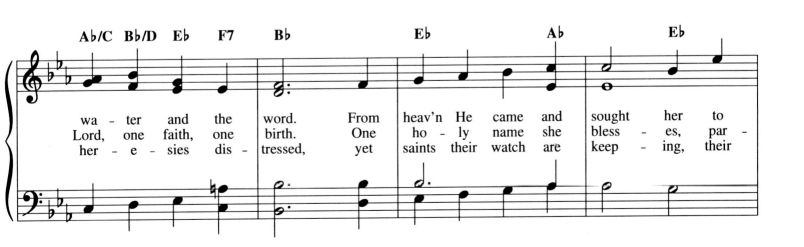

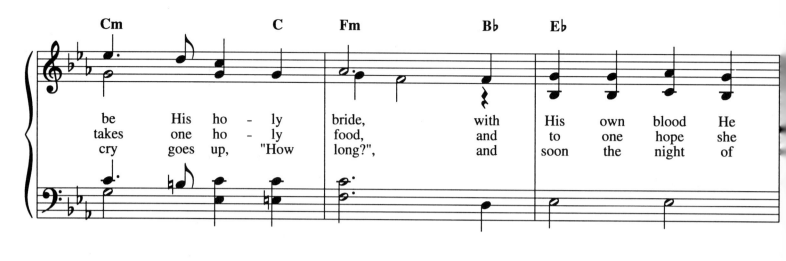

be His ho – ly bride, with His own blood He
takes one ho – ly food, and to one hope she
cry goes up, "How long?", and soon the night of

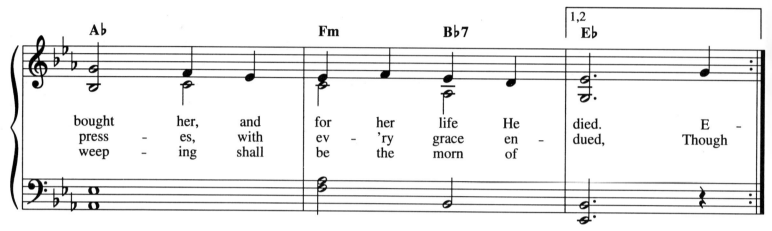

bought her, and for her life He died. E –
press – es, with ev – 'ry grace en – dued, Though
weep – ing shall be the morn of

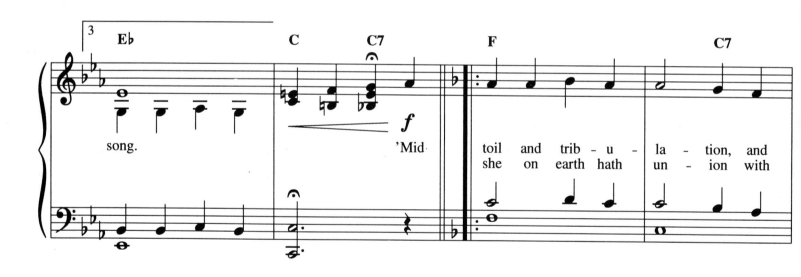

song. 'Mid toil and trib – u – la – tion, and
she on earth hath un – ion with

tu – mult of her war, she waits her con – sum –
God the three in one, and mys – tic sweet com –

ma - tion of peace for ev - er more. 'Til
mun - ion with those whose rest is won: O

with the vi - sion glo - rious her
hap - py ones and ho - ly! her Lord,

long - ing eyes are
give us grace that

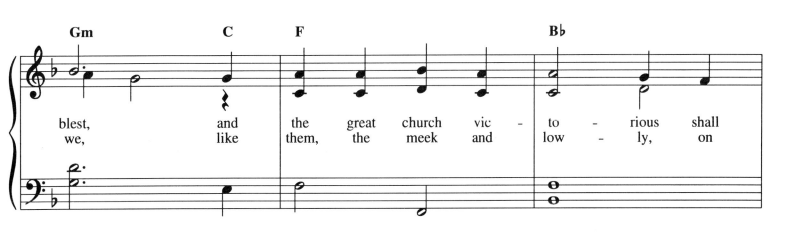

blest, and the great church vic - to - rious shall
we, like them, the church meek and low - ly, on

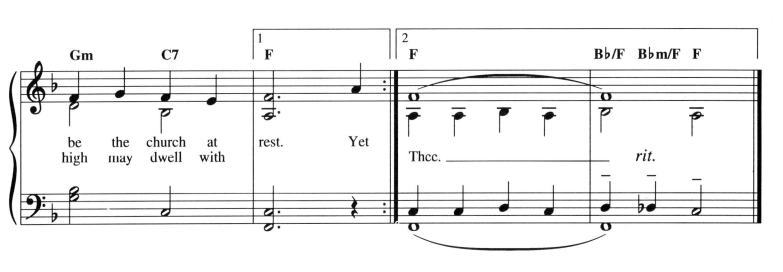

be the church at rest. Yet
high may dwell with

Thee. _____ rit.

195

... *I* am the light
of the world:
he that followeth me
shall not walk
in darkness,
but shall have
the light of life.

JOHN 8:12

THE OLD RUGGED CROSS

In the fall of 1912, George Bennard began writing this hymn. A traveling evangelist, Bennard was conducting revivals that fall in the states of Michigan and New York. The completed song was given to Homer Rodeheaver, the popular song leader for Billy Sunday, and its fame spread rapidly. Two years before Bennard's death in Reed City, Michigan, the Chamber of Commerce erected a wooden cross 12 feet high to honor him and the song he wrote.

THE OLD RUGGED CROSS

George Bennard, 1913

On a

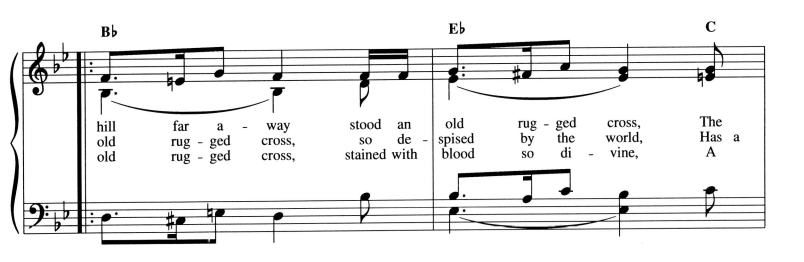

hill   far a - way   stood an   old   rug - ged   cross,   The
old   rug - ged   cross,   so de - spised   by the   world,   Has a
old   rug - ged   cross,   stained with   blood   so di - vine,   A

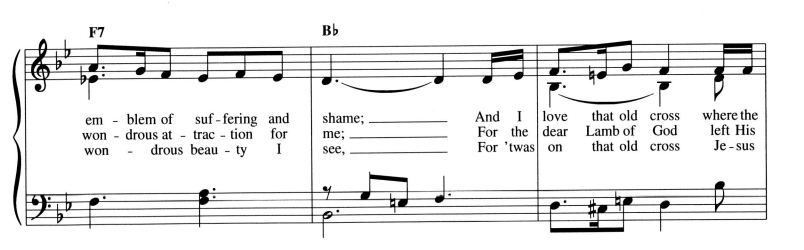

em - blem of   suf - fering and   shame; _____   And I   love   that old cross   where the
won - drous at - trac - tion   for   me; _____   For the   dear   Lamb of God   left His
won - drous beau - ty   I   see, _____   For 'twas   on   that old cross   Je - sus

dear - est and best — For a
glo - ry a - bove, — To
suf - fered and died, — To

world of lost sin - ners was
bear it to dark Cal - va -
par - don and sanc - ti - fy

slain. _____
ry. _____
me. _____

So I'll cher - ish the old rug - ged

cross, _____ Till my tro - phies at last I lay

down; _____ I will cling to the old rug - ged cross, _____ And ex -

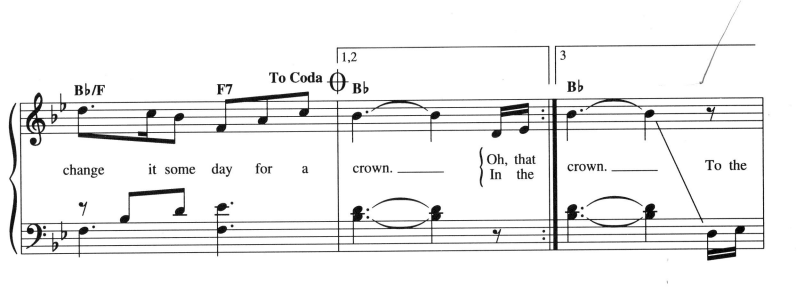

change it some day for a | crown. _____ Oh, that / In the | crown. _____ To the

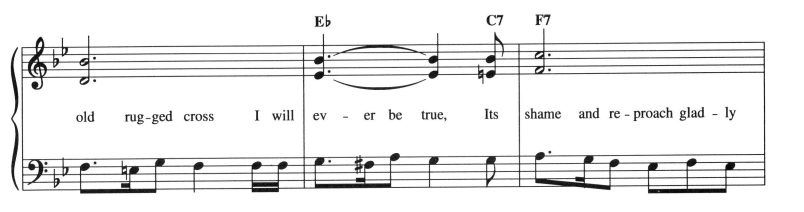

old rug-ged cross I will ev – er be true, Its shame and re - proach glad - ly

bear; _____ Then He'll call me some day to my home far a - way, Where His

glo - ry for - ev - er I'll | share. _____ So I'll

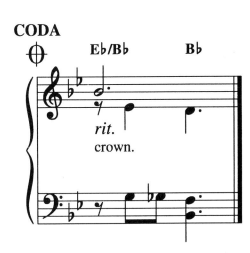

rit.
crown.

HIS IS MY FATHER'S WORLD

Maltbie D. Babcock, a baseball pitcher in college and a varsity swimmer, wrote the hymn in 1901. Ordained to the Presbyterian ministry, he became pastor of New York City's Brick Presbyterian Church. His strong personality, his friendliness, and his ability as a preacher greatly endeared him to his congregation and the community. The hymn, which initially seems to focus on the beauties of nature, ultimately proves to have a higher subject in view: the God who is sovereign over all.

THIS IS MY FATHER'S WORLD

TERRA PATRIS
Franklin L. Sheppard, 1915

Maltbie D. Babcock, 1901

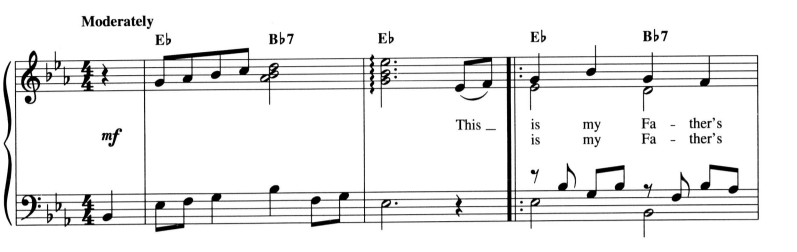

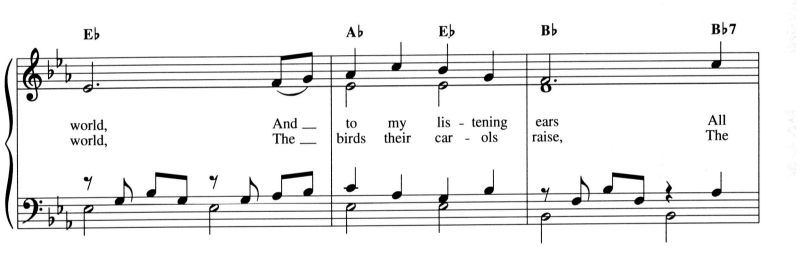

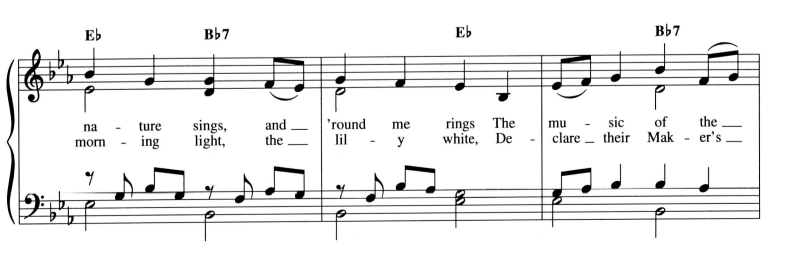

201

get That though the wrong seems ___ oft so strong, God is ___ the Rul - er ___ yet. *rit.* This *a tempo* is my Fa - ther's world; The ___ bat - tle is not done; Je - sus who died shall be sat - is - fied, And earth ___ and heav'n be ___ one.

E GATHER TOGETHER

The turmoil and strife in the struggle for political freedom in the
Netherlands in the first half of the seventeenth century inspired
the Dutch hymn asking God's blessings on the people's yearning
for freedom. These words and music of unknown origin were
forgotten for two and a half centuries until they were published
in Vienna in 1877. Theodore Baker, an American scholar, made
the English translation in 1894.

WE GATHER TOGETHER

KREMSER
Netherlands Folk Melody
harm. Edward Kremser, 1877

Anon., 16th century
tr. Theodore Baker, 1894

gath - er to - geth - er to ask the Lord's bless - ing; He
side us to guide us, our God with us join - ing, Or -

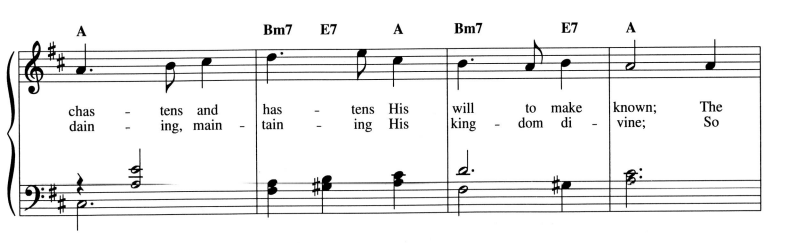

chas - tens and has - tens His will to make known; The
dain - ing, main - tain - ing His king - dom di - vine; The So

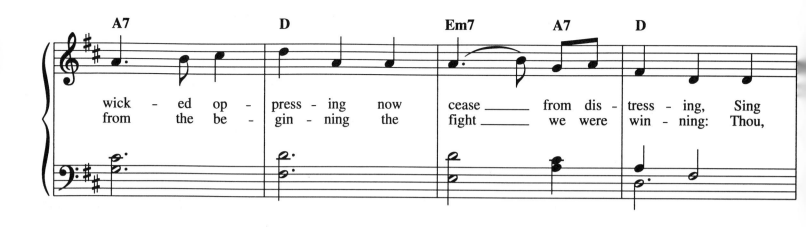

wicked op - pressing now cease _____ from dis - tress - ing, Sing
from the be - gin - ning now the fight _____ we were win - ning: Thou,

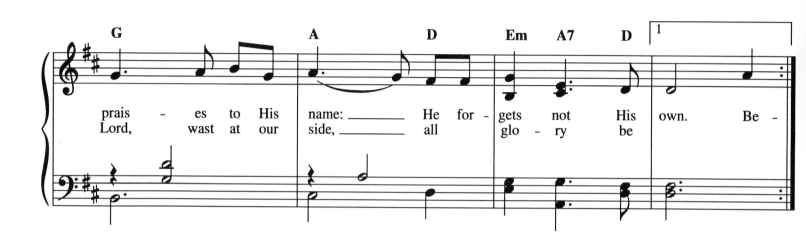

prais - es to His name: _____ He for - gets not His own. Be -
Lord, wast at our side, _____ all glo - ry His be

Thine!

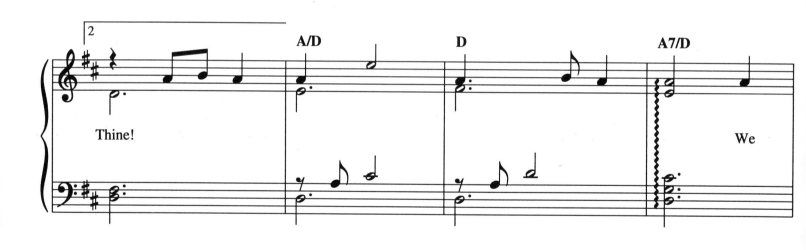

We

all do ex - toll Thee, Thou Lead - er tri - um - phant, And

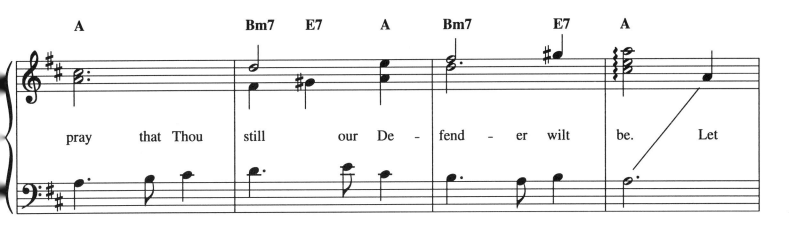

pray   that Thou   still   our De - fend - er wilt   be. _____ Let

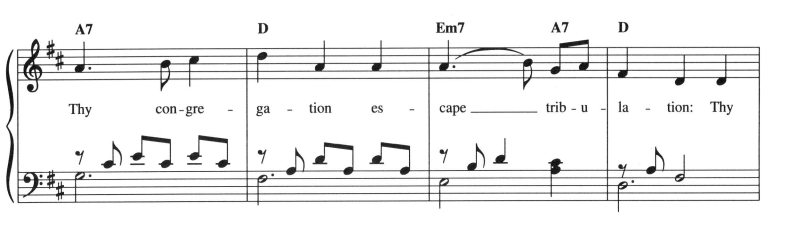

Thy   con - gre -   ga - tion   es -   cape _____ trib - u - la - tion: Thy

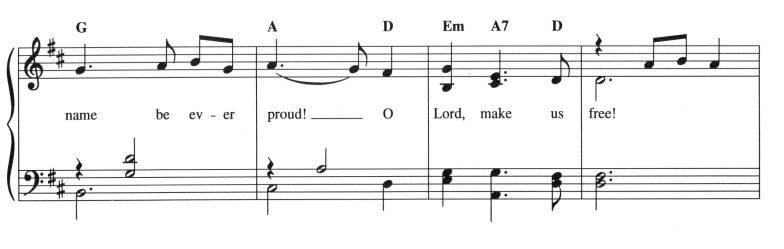

name   be ev - er   proud! _____   O   Lord, make   us   free!

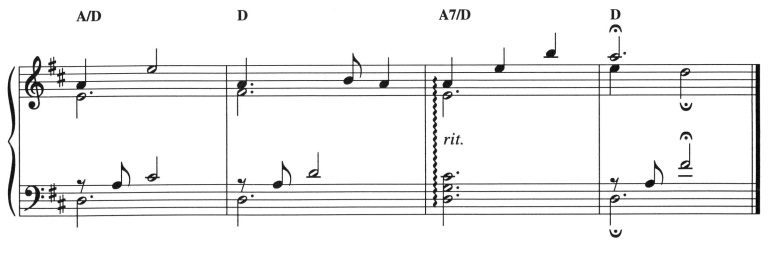

rit.

 HAT A FRIEND WE HAVE IN JESUS

Joseph Scriven, a native of Ireland, moved to Canada when he was 25 years old. Twice he experienced great tragedy. In England, his bride-to-be drowned the day before the wedding, and in Canada he fell in love with one Eliza Roche, who died suddenly before they were married. Scriven wrote his mother in Ireland of Eliza's death and enclosed the poem "What A Friend We Have In Jesus," which he had written in his sorrow. At his death in 1886, he was buried next to the grave of Eliza Roche in the community of Bewdley.

WHAT A FRIEND WE HAVE IN JESUS

Joseph Scriven, 1855

CONVERSE
Charles C. Converse, 1868

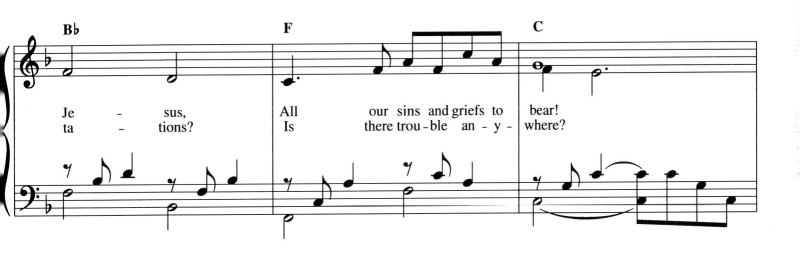

prayer!
prayer.
O
Can
what peace we of - ten for - feit,
we find a friend so faith - ful

O
Who
what need - less pain to bear,
will all our sor - rows share?
All
Je - sus knows our ev - 'ry
be - cause we do not

car - ry
weak - ness,
Ev - 'ry-thing to God in
Take it to the Lord in
prayer!
prayer.

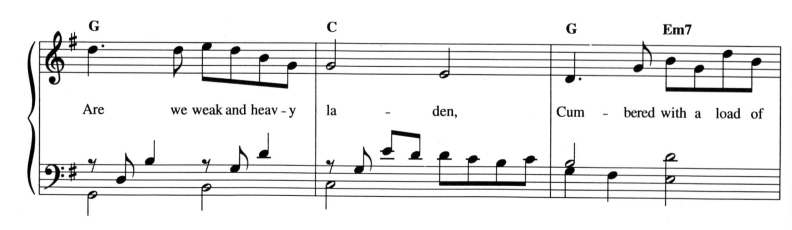

Are we weak and heav - y la - den,
Cum - bered with a load of

211

WHEN I SURVEY THE WONDROUS CROSS

The apostle Paul, writing to the churches in Galatia, assured them that they were not obligated to observe the requirements of Mosaic Law, nor should they glory in performing these rituals. Then he said, "but God forbid that I should glory, save in the cross of our Lord Jesus Christ, by whom the world is crucified unto me, and I unto the world" (Gal. 6:14). In writing this hymn in 1707, Isaac Watts captured the essence of Paul's admonition, concluding with a statement of personal commitment.

WHEN I SURVEY THE WONDROUS CROSS

Isaac Watts, 1707

HAMBURG
Lowell Mason, 1824

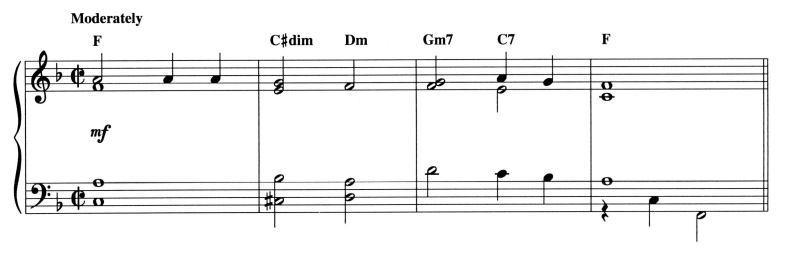

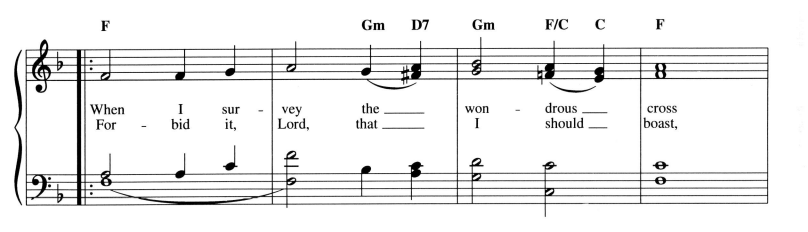

When I sur- vey the ___ won - drous ___ cross
For- bid it, Lord, that ___ I should ___ boast,

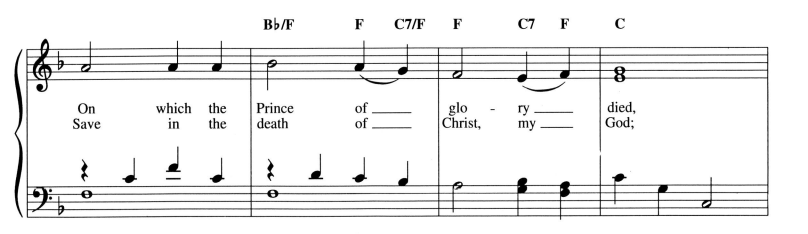

On which the Prince of ___ glo - ry ___ died,
Save in the death of ___ Christ, my ___ God;

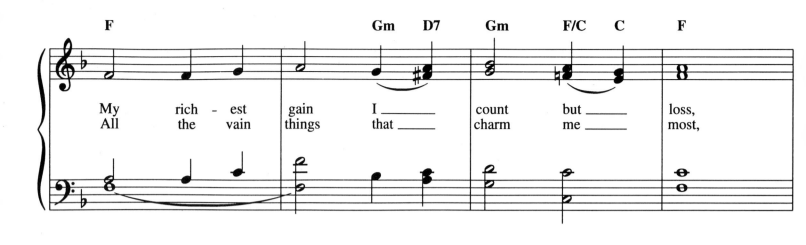

My   rich - est   gain   I _____   count   but _____   loss,
All   the   vain   things   that _____   charm   me _____   most,

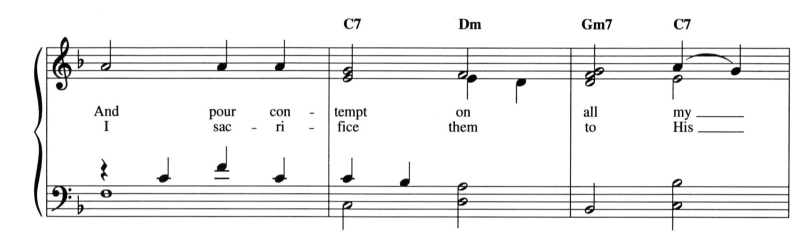

And   pour con - tempt   on   all   my _____
I   sac - ri - fice   on   them   to   His _____

pride.   blood.   See,   from   His
Were   the   whole

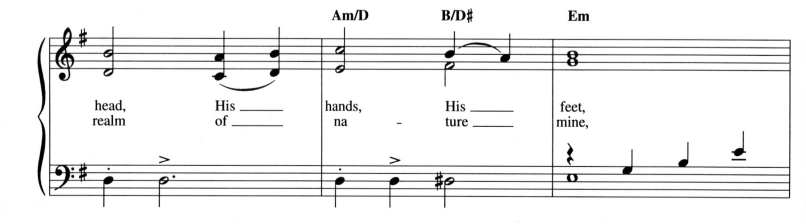

head,   His _____   hands,   His _____   feet,
realm   of _____   na - ture _____   mine,

214

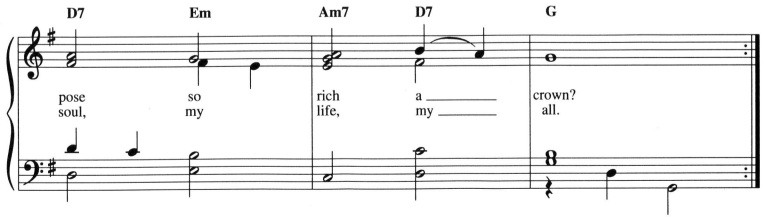

215

*I will praise thee, O Lord, among the peoples,
I will sing praises to thee among the nations.*

PSALM 108:3

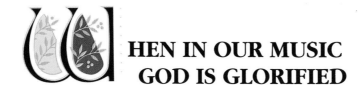

WHEN IN OUR MUSIC GOD IS GLORIFIED

This hymn, which speaks about the sound of music glorifying
God, was written in 1972 by Fred Pratt Green, a Methodist
minister in England. The unusual meter of 10.10.10. with Alleluia,
and the rhyme scheme *aaab*, reveal a well-crafted text. Stanza
four refers to the hymn sung by Jesus and his disciples at the
Last Supper. Stanza five brings reminders of the magnificent
Psalm 150, praising God with instruments and voices.

WHEN IN OUR MUSIC GOD IS GLORIFIED

Fred Pratt Green, 1972

ENGELBERG
Charles V. Stanford, 1905

With jubilance

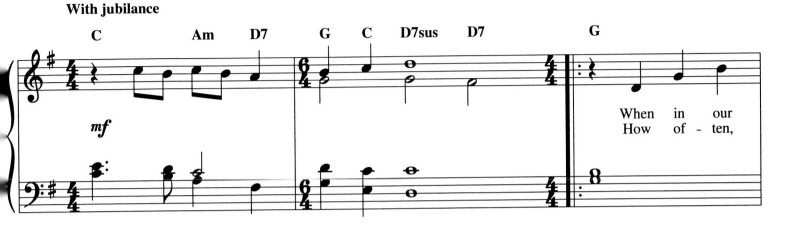

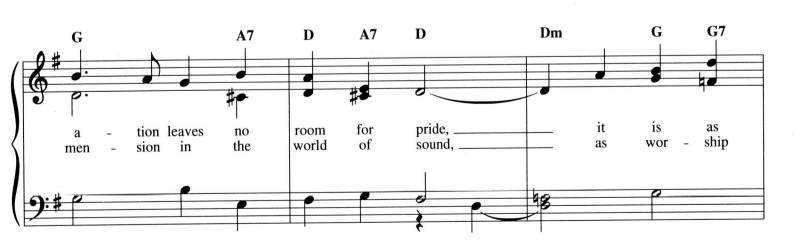

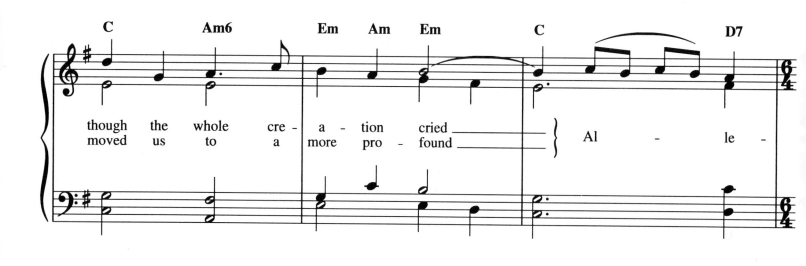

though the whole cre - a - tion cried ____ } Al - le -
moved us to a more pro - found ____

lu - ia! So has the Church, in lit - ur -
And did not Je - sus sing a

gy and song, ____ in faith and love, through cen - tu -
psalm that night ____ when ut - most e - vil strove a -

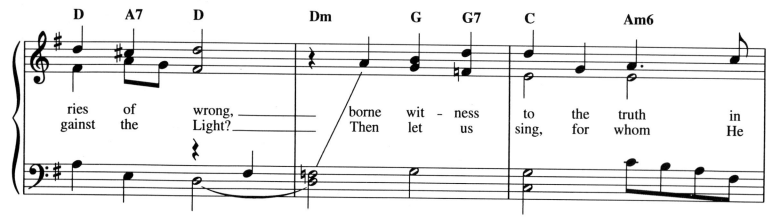

ries of wrong, ____ borne wit - ness to the truth in
gainst of the Light? ____ Then let us sing, for whom He

O sing to the Lord a new song;
sing to the Lord, all the earth!

PSALM 96:1
(RSVB)

HEN THE ROLL IS CALLED UP YONDER

James M. Black, a member of the Pine Street Methodist Church, Williamsport, Pennsylvania, was a singing-school teacher. He taught a Sunday school class and enlisted young people to join this class. One teenage girl he had enlisted did not answer her name when he called the roll. At the moment he mentioned that when his name would be called in heaven, he wanted to be there to respond. When he returned home, this thought lingered in his mind. In a few minutes he wrote the stanzas and refrain, then sat down at the piano and completed the tune. It was published in 1892.

220

WHEN THE ROLL IS CALLED UP YONDER

James M. Black, 1893

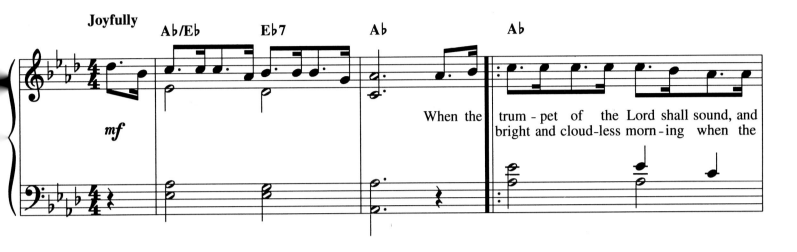

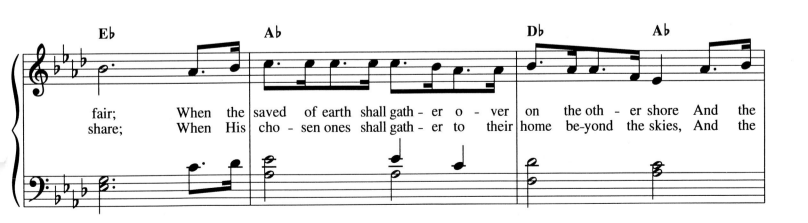

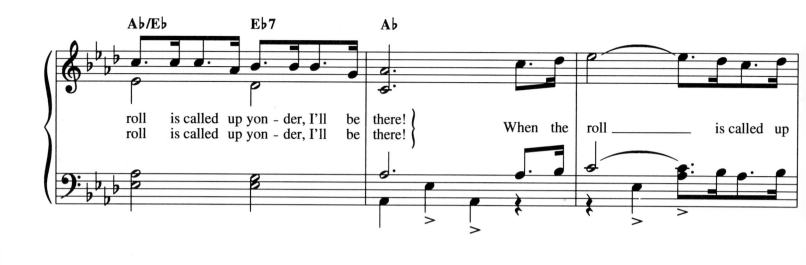

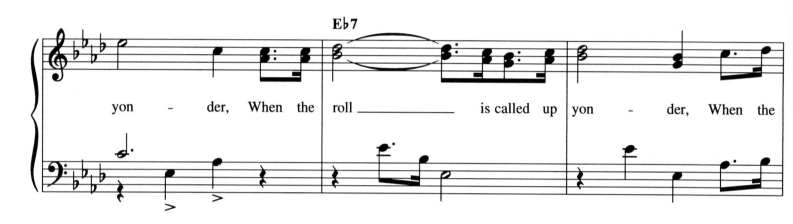

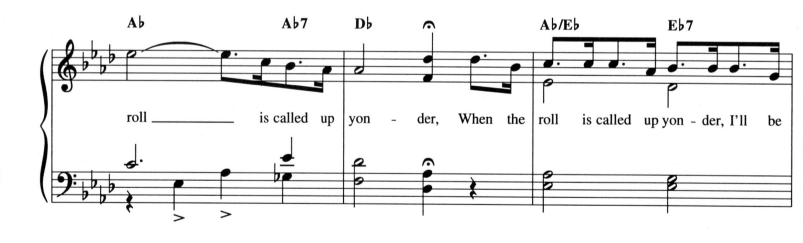

talk of all His won-drous love and care; Then when all of life is o-ver and our

work on earth is done And the roll is called up yon-der, I'll be there! When the

roll _____ is called up yon - der, When the roll _____ is called up yon - der, When the

roll _____ is called up yon - der, When the roll is called up yon-der, I'll be there!